Rudolf Steiner
on
NUTRITION and STIMULANTS

ISBN 0-938250-29-9

Printed in U.S.A.

Typeset by An Grianán, Calais

 printed on
recycled fibre

Rudolf Steiner
on
NUTRITION and STIMULANTS

Lectures and Extracts
compiled and translated by

K. Castelliz
and
B. Saunders-Davies

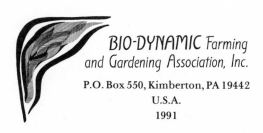

BIO-DYNAMIC Farming
and Gardening Association, Inc.
P.O. Box 550, Kimberton, PA 19442
U.S.A.
1991

CONTENTS

PART II
From Other Lectures, Lecture Cycles and Books

(a) From lectures given to Members of the
Anthroposophical Society.

PART III
*From an early lecture given to Members of the
Theosophical Society.*

TRANSLATORS' FOREWORD

With the numerous and varied theories about diets circulating these days, many people want to know exactly what Rudolf Steiner said on the question of nutrition and what he did not say. We have endeavoured to compile everything relevant from as many lectures and written works as possible. Inevitably there is a certain amount of repetition as lectures were given to different audiences.

Everything, except for one lecture, has been newly translated, partly to preserve a certain unity of style and partly to simplify questions of copyright. We would like to thank the Anthroposophic Press, Spring Valley, New York for permission to use Maria St.Goar's translation of 'Problems of Nutrition'. Many of the lectures to the workmen were only available in typescript or not translated and therefore not easily accessible to English-speaking readers. Rudolf Steiner spoke to the workmen in a very familiar colloquial style which we have endeavoured to retain. At times he used quite earthy expressions which he would not have permitted himself in front of his usual anthroposophical audiences! He also dealt rather ruthlessly with materialistic academic professors of the day, probably to discourage his craftsmen listeners from being overawed by the magic word 'scientific' and prevent them being carried away by the wave of popular scientific theory which was poured out to the masses by lesser minds. For true scientific method and the discoveries of scientific observation he always had the greatest respect.

The notes on milling seem to take one back to bygone days. The old water mills worked according to realities which were recognised by Rudolf Steiner and no adequate substitute has as yet been found. Some modern mills are better than

others but they run off motors, electric or internal combustion, and therefore lack rhythm. The atmosphere of
sanctity in an old mill may seem exaggerated to people
today, but some of us can well remember the solemn mood
one encountered on entering such a mill. One spoke quietly
and listened to the gentle rhythm. What Rudolf Steiner said
was quite comprehensible to the people concerned. These
notes make one realise how today's bread is often ruined from
beginning to end — growing, milling and baking. One can
also see how, with care and understanding, man could live
better on much less.

PUBLISHER'S FOREWORD

The Bio-Dynamic Association would like to express its gratitude
to Barbara Saunders-Davies and Katherine Castelliz for their selfless labors in making the material available in English. Out of
their own initiative and financial resources they prepared this
text. Consequently, American readers will notice British spelling
and some expressions in the text.

It should be noted that these lectures were presented to an
audience that was quite familiar with anthroposophical concepts.
Many of the extracts would be easy to misunderstand if the reader
did not have the context out of which they were presented.
Therefore, we recommend that new readers first obtain Steiner's
basic books so that this study material will be more rewarding.

PART I

From Lectures given to the Workmen at the Goetheanum, Dornach, Switzerland, from the 5th of August 1922 to the 24th of September 1924.

MILK FOR CHILDREN

Extract from a
Lecture to the Workmen   Dornach, 5th August 1922

Man must be able to feed himself and breathe in order to become a being that feels; and in order to become a thinking being he has to draw forces from the cosmos. It does not happen of itself that he can think or learn to speak. He can no more think his own self than he can eat his own self.

Let us take a closer look at what happens. We will begin by making clear what exactly takes place when we take in food, have it in a more or less dead condition in our intestines, then revivify it by means of the lymph glands and through the lymph carry it into the blood which is then renewed through the breathing process. The blood or rather the force of the blood, the pressure of the breath, ascends through the spinal marrow into the brain and there unites with the activity of the brain.

You only need to observe the difference between the nourishment of a child and an adult to learn a great deal about the whole nature of man. As you know, in very early life a child has to drink a lot of milk. At first it takes only milk. What is the significance of this — that the child only takes milk? We can appreciate this if we understand what milk consists of.

One does not usually realise that the average milk consists of 84% water. So when as children we drink milk we are actually drinking 84% water and only the remaining 16% consists of other substances. Of this 16% only 4% is albumin, 6% fat and the remainder is residual substances such as salt, etc. Basically that is what the child takes in with milk — mainly water.

Now I have already told you that man consists mainly of fluid. The child must increase this fluid constantly [in its body]. It has to grow and needs much water for this, and it takes this water in with its milk.

You might say: Then it would be the same if we gave the child the 16% of solid food and the rest to drink as water.

But you see the human body is not designed for that. What we get in milk is not just 16% of ordinary albumin, fat, etc. but albumin and fat that are dissolved in the milk, dissolved in water when it is given to the child as milk.

So when the child drinks milk it gets the substances that it needs in a soluble state. It is quite different if the body has first to do the work of dissolving.

If you remember what I have already said about nutrition* you will say: The foodstuffs that we take through the mouth we must first dissolve. Nature only allows us to take solid food as far as the mouth; then we dissolve it with our own fluids. The rest of the body, stomach, intestines, etc. can only use dissolved substances.

The child has first to acquire this capacity of dissolving. He cannot do this at first by himself. To begin with it is done for him beforehand. You can understand from this that if the child is given too much artificially compounded food, it immediately has an effect on him.

Now you might say: If I were able to produce artificial milk, if I could combine 16% of albumin, fat, etc. with water so that outwardly it resembled milk, this would be as good for the child as the milk he requires.

This however is not the case. It would have a stunting effect on the child. Such a product would be very damaging to mankind. So what can bring about the dissolving process

---

* Rudolf Steiner had already given some talks to the workmen of which no shorthand notes were taken.

that the child requires? Only life itself. As a last resort animals can do it, but not all animals. For the very earliest part of its life while the child is not yet able to dissolve albumin and fat for himself he can only rightly be fed with human milk.

Of other milks, asses milk is the nearest to human milk. So if for some reason it is altogether impossible for the mother or a foster mother to suckle the child, asses milk would be the next best thing. It sounds very amusing but actually it is asses milk which most resembles human milk! So if breast feeding is not possible it can, if need be, be replaced by keeping a jenny in the stable, and thus providing milk for the child! This is of course purely hypothetical and I say this just to show how things are connected in Nature.

If for instance you compare milk with, say, hen's eggs as a foodstuff, you will find that hens eggs contain about 14% protein; thus far more, indeed four times more than milk. If one starts to give the child such food containing so much protein, the child itself must have acquired this capacity of dissolving. So you see how necessary it is that the child gets fluid food. But what sort of fluid food? A fluid food that has already gone through a life process and is if possible still alive, as when coming from the mother's breast.

It is quite clear that when the child drinks milk and it passes via the mouth and gullet into the stomach (where it is first killed) it can then be re-vivified in the intestines. So in the child we can see that life must first be killed, and because this life is only slightly changed the child needs less strength to re-vivify milk than if it eats other things. You see from this how close man is to life.

From this you can also see something else. If one really thinks things through where does it lead you? Start from this point. If we say: The child must take in living food which it can kill and re-vivify of itself, and then we say: Man consists mainly of fluid — can we then say: Man consists of water, of that water which we find outside in nature, in lifeless nature? If that were so then this water that we find

3

in lifeless nature would have to work in the child as it does in the adult who has already accumulated more life forces.

But from this you see that the 90% of water that we carry in us is not ordinary lifeless water but it is living water, enlivened water. What man bears within him as water is something different, it is living water.... So if you say: I have water in the stream and I have water in the human body it would be just as if you said: There I have a corpse and there I have a living person. The water in the stream is the corpse of the water that is in the human body.

This is why we say that man has a life body within him. Man has not only this dead physical substance in him, but he has also a life body. This is what real thinking arrives at: Man has this life body within him.

COFFEE AND TEA

Extract from a
Lecture to the Workmen   Dornach, 9th August 1922

A person may feel: I cannot think properly, I cannot collect my thoughts. A journalist who has to write an article every day can easily get this feeling. Well, writing an article every day means dissolving a terrible lot of brain sand. To have to write an article every day is a terrible thing because it means dissolving a terrible lot of brain sand. So one begins — at least it used to be so — one begins to chew one's pen. One used to say — particularly about journalists — that they sucked their pens to get the last bit of inspiration out of them. By chewing something one gets the last bit of strength out of the body into the head to master this brain sand. Much brain sand has to be dissolved.

All this takes place instinctively. Obviously the journalist does not say: I chew my pen in order to get thoughts. But this goes on. His instinct takes him to the coffee house and he drinks black coffee. He does not think about all this, because journalists know nothing about these processes. But once they have drunk their black coffee — good heavens, suddenly it works! They can write again after the coffee. Why is this? It is because in the black coffee there is what is called caffeine. This is a substance which contains much nitrogen. Nitrogen is contained in the air. We get it all the time. We breathe in a certain amount of oxygen and nitrogen. A person who has to dissolve brain sand needs a force which is especially found in nitrogen. From the nitrogen we get the strength to dissolve our brain sand.

At night, when we are asleep, we are much more exposed

to nitrogen than when we are awake. If we breathe in more oxygen we live quicker; if we breathe in more nitrogen we would live slower. We could then dissolve more brain sand because we would have more time in which to do it. The journalist who drinks coffee, reckons quite unconsciously with the extra nitrogen he gets. The extra nitrogen he gets from the caffeine enables him to create more brain sand and to dissolve it. He no longer needs to chew his pen, he can write with it, because now once again his thoughts follow one another.

You see how the human ego works. Because we take nitrogen-rich food into the stomach the ego can carry caffeine up into the brain and this nitrogen makes it easier for us to dissolve the brain sand and enables us to make one thought follow another.

Some people have the peculiarity that their thoughts are too coherent. They cannot get away from their thoughts. They have the inherent tendency always to be working on their brain sand. They would be well advised to do the opposite. While one person's thoughts are concentrated and he can develop a coherent train of thought, another has to resort to the caffeine in coffee to help him.

A person who does not want his thoughts to be concentrated but wants them to sparkle and scintillate, who likes to throw off witty remarks which appear clever — he drinks tea. It has the opposite effect. It scatters the thoughts. It promotes a different kind of dissolution of the brain sand.

All these things that go on in us are really very interesting and complicated. Every foodstuff works in a different way and we must always correct what is about to arise by adding its opposite. We have to dissolve it. It is the highest spiritual entity within us which is continually dissolving our person inwardly, one might say.

If someone, over a period of time, eats too little nitrogen-containing food, then it will happen that he will easily feel sleepy. One of your questions referred to this. This is caused by too little nitrogen in the food, and therefore if we tend to feel sleepy, we should try to eat more nitrogen-rich foods. This can be done in many different ways. By eating cheese, protein foods or eggs, for instance, the nitrogen level in us will be improved. Man must be given what he needs in order that his ego can do its work.... Our brain must contain the necessary substances for the ego to work in it.... If we could not dissolve ourselves, we would not be able to think and not acquire ego-consciousness. What we call ego-consciousness arises in this process of dissolution.

MILK FOR CHILDREN

Extract from a
Lecture to the Workmen   Dornach, 13th September 1922

The baby is best fed on its own mother's milk. It has itself come out of the mother's body. It is therefore understandable that its whole organism, its whole body, is closely connected with the mother. The child will thrive best if, when it comes into the world, it does not get anything other than what is connected with its mother's body.

It can happen however that the mother's milk is not suitable, due to its composition. Some human milk, for instance, is bitter or too salty. In this case the best alternative would be milk provided by another person. The question can arise: Cannot the child be fed with cows' milk from the start? The answer is that for the new-born baby, cows' milk is not very good. But one need not think that it is a terrible crime against the human organism if one feeds the child with cows' milk suitably diluted, etc. Obviously milk from cows and goats etc. is different from human milk but not so different that one cannot use cows' milk instead of human milk. As long as the child drinks only milk, nothing has to be chewed, consequently certain organs of the body are much more active than they will be later when solid food is eaten. Milk is fundamentally still alive when the child drinks it. It is almost liquid life that the child imbibes.

* * * * *

The baby does not look out into the world very much, and if it does, it does not know what it sees. But all the more does it look inward with its feeling. The baby feels immediately if there is something in the milk which does not belong to it and which has to be thrown out into the intestines so that it can be excreted. And if something is not right with the milk, the liver will receive a tendency for an illness which will express itself in later life.

THE PROCESS OF NUTRITION

From a
Lecture to the Workmen   Dornach, 16th September 1922

In order to get a more complete picture, we shall have to study in more detail certain processes in the human body which recur daily. One can only understand higher processes if one really comprehends certain lower processes. Therefore today I will once again go over the whole process of nutrition from the physical, material point of view as well as from the aspect of the soul.

We eat, and when we eat, the food first goes into our mouth. We take in solid and liquid foods. Food from the air we take in via the breath through the lungs. So let us consider solid and liquid foods. Our body can only deal with fluids. Therefore all solid food must be dissolved into fluid in the mouth. This can only be done because the palate and the whole of the mouth have small organs, known as glands, which secrete saliva.

So you must imagine that, for instance, on the edge of the tongue there are these small glands. They are little things arranged in such a way that under the microscope they look like small grapes. They are made up of cells. These glands secrete saliva. The saliva dissolves the foodstuffs and mingles with them. The food must be mixed with saliva or else it is of no use to the human organism.

Now here we have an activity — the blending of food with saliva is an activity — and the result of this activity is taste. We taste our food. During the mixing of our food with saliva, we exercise the sense of taste. As we perceive colours with our eyes, so we perceive the taste of food with our sense of taste. So we say that in the mouth the food is mixed with saliva and is tasted. Taste gives us an awareness of foods. Mixing with saliva prepares the food so that the rest of the body can deal with it.

Saliva must contain a certain substance, otherwise the food cannot be prepared so that it is fit for the stomach. This substance is there and it is called ptyalin. The salivary glands secrete this ptyalin. And this is the first substance to work on the food and make it usable for the stomach.

The food thus prepared goes by way of the gullet to the stomach. In the stomach it must be further worked on. To do this there must be another substance in the stomach. The stomach secretes it. As the mouth produces saliva containing ptyalin, so the stomach produces another kind of saliva. The saliva of the stomach contains a different substance. The food gets mixed with the saliva of the stomach. The stomach produces pepsin instead of ptyalin.

Adults and children over seven years old have no sense of taste in their stomachs, but the baby tastes food in its stomach as the adult tastes it in his mouth. But one has to take account of the soul nature of the baby if one wants to understand the whole man. The adult can only get an idea of what this taste in the stomach is like when the stomach is out of order and its contents move upwards instead of downwards. Then one gets an idea that there is a sense of taste in the stomach. I take it that at least some of you have had this experience of something that was already in the stomach coming back into the mouth, and you will know that this had a worse taste than almost anything you have ever eaten. Anything that tasted like what comes up from the stomach you would not fancy. One would not eat anything with such a taste. But the taste of this chyme must have come about in some way. It comes about in the stomach. In the mouth the food is only mixed with ptyalin, in the stomach with pepsin and the result is the different taste. Taste is altogether a strange thing.

Imagine you are very sensitive to taste and you drink water. Unless it is contaminated, water does not on the whole have a bad taste. But if you put a lot of sugar on your tongue and let it dissolve, then it can happen that the water will have an acid taste. Of course you must be somewhat sensitive to this. Taste is a strange thing. We adults taste our food in the mouth but before this develops we taste in the stomach. The child therefore should have such foods as will not taste too bad in the stomach — mother's milk or milk in general. This does not take on a very bad taste in the stomach because the child has a close relationship with milk. Before it was born it was part of the body that produces its milk. So the child feels connected with milk. Therefore milk does not produce a bad taste for it. If the small child gets other food too soon it will find it nauseating. This does not apply to the adult, because his taste has become coarser. But the child finds it nauseating because he is not related to foods from outside.

Now you see, from the stomach, food mixed with pepsin goes into the intestines — small intestine, large intestine, and so on. The chyme spreads in the intestines.

If the chyme would spread in the intestines and nothing further happen to it, it would form a hard stony mass which would soon be the end of man. So something further happens to the chyme.

This again is done by a gland. There are glands in the mouth, glands in the stomach and then there is a large gland behind the stomach. If you look at a person from the front, this fairly large gland is behind the stomach. This gland which one calls the pancreas also secretes a kind of saliva and this passes through fine ducts into the intestines. So in the intestines the food is mixed with a kind of saliva for the third time. The substance which the pancreas secretes is transformed within us. First the pancreas secretes it. There it is almost the same as the pepsin in the stomach, but on its way to the intestines it is transformed. It becomes stronger. The foodstuffs must be more strongly attacked and this stronger type of saliva substance which is secreted by the pancreas is called trypsin. So the pancreas secretes trypsin; at least it secretes something which in the intestines becomes the strong juice, trypsin. Thus the chyme is mixed with this, and something new happens to it.

We can no longer be aware of this consciously in our head, but what arises from the chyme is now tasted or felt by the liver and thought over by the kidneys. So everything that goes on in the intestines is thought over by the kidneys and taken cognisance of by the liver. There is something of a soul nature in the kidneys and liver and this perceives in the same way as man does in his head. But we know nothing of it. At the most — as I told you last time — when we dream, something of it comes into our consciousness in the form of pictures. The way the chyme winds snake-like through the intestines and mixes with the trypsin produces a certain animation and man perceives it in his dreams as snakes. It is a projection of a vague unclear soul element that man perceives.

Now the liver which is aware of the whole story of the trypsin, ptyalin and pepsin — I must put it like this because unfortunately science has given these awful names, and since anyway we do not get any sympathy from science when we explain these things, how much more exasperation would we cause if we gave new names! One could give new names but to save science undue consternation one does not, but goes on using the old names — ptyalin, pepsin, trypsin. So three times our food is mixed with some sort of saliva; the third time gives rise to a 'liver-feeling'. So we can write:

mouth   : taste, ptyalin
stomach : small child's taste, pepsin
pancreas: liver-feeling, trypsin

What this liver-feeling is you can get a good idea of if you recall what it is like if you hold a very strong onion under your nose. The tears come, do they not? Or if you put horseradish under your nose the tears come. Why does this happen? It is because the horseradish and the onion act on the tear glands and the tear glands secrete the bitter tears. It is somewhat similar with the chyme in the intestines, and the liver secretes gall like the glands of the eyes secrete tears when we sniff onions and horseradish. The onion must be smelled if it is to produce tears and the chyme must be felt by the liver if it is to produce gall to mix with it. This is the fourth mixing:

liver: gall

After the mouth has worked with its ptyalin, the stomach with its pepsin, the pancreas with its trypsin, the liver adds its gall to the chyme in the intestines. Only then comes the thinking process of the kidneys.

When the chyme is prepared in this way, mixed four times with a kind of saliva, it makes its way through the walls of the intestines into the lymph vessels and from there into the blood. We can truly say that within the human body there is an extraordinarily complicated life-process transforming the chyme on its way from the mouth into the blood stream. The chyme is constantly transformed so that it can be digested in the right way, not only by the stomach but by the whole body.

This is done in various ways. Imagine if you were in a chemical laboratory, even if you were a very clever professor, and had to do all this. You would not be able to, if you first had to mix the food with the mouth saliva, then with the stomach saliva, then with the intestinal saliva and then with the gall. All this happens within you. You do it constantly every day, but if you had to do it in the laboratory you would not be able to. Man has intelligence, but what happens intelligently in his abdomen is far more clever than any man on earth. It is a very wise and ingenious process that takes place within us. It cannot easily be copied.

But you will have even greater respect for this process when I describe its details. What does man eat? He eats plant substances, animal substances and mineral substances and so gets a great variety of substances into his mouth, stomach and intestines and they all have to be transformed by the different juices.

Imagine you eat potatoes. When you eat potatoes ask yourself, what do they consist of? Potatoes consist mainly of starch. You know that starch is derived mainly from potatoes. So you really eat starch when you eat potatoes. This is the first thing. You eat starch. There are many things closely related to starch. The potato consists almost entirely of starch but also contains various liquids, mainly water. And because it is alive, not dead, the potato looks as it does. It is living starch and therefore, as I have told you, it must be killed. Then it is pure starch. Everywhere one finds starch in plants. Whenever you eat plants there is always starch in them.

What else do you eat? Whether you take it from the plant kingdom or the animal kingdom, you eat protein. If you eat an ordinary egg, you get albumen in its pure state but it is killed within you. You also eat protein in meat and in plants. You eat protein all the time. This is the second thing we eat: protein and protein-like substances.

The third thing we eat is very different from starch and protein, it is fats. Fats are quite different from starch and protein. There is not so much fat in plants as in animals. There are of course plant fats. Man must have fats either from the plant or animal kingdom if he wants to feed himself properly. So, fats are the third food that man needs.

The fourth thing is the salts in food. We either have to eat foods which contain enough salts of their own or else we put a salt cellar on the table and we help ourselves either with our fingers, or with a horn spoon or with the tip of our knives and add it to the soup or other food. It is eaten. We need it. That is the fourth thing that is eaten

15

— salts. I have to write salts, because there are various different salts.

Starch
Protein
Fats
Salts

All this goes into the intestine and is transformed there.

Now what comes of all this? Because the foods are well-prepared by the mouth saliva and the stomach saliva, they can, in the intestines, be mixed for the third time with a sort of saliva and they do not become hard but are changed into something different.

What becomes of starch? Starch becomes sugar. So when you eat starch you will have sugar in your stomach. If we want to have sugar in us we do not need to eat it. We would not need any if we made enough ourselves, because we *can* make sugar ourselves. But we are so made that we cannot make everything, though our nature is such that we can do a lot. It so happens that we do not make enough sugar — some people not nearly enough — and therefore extra sugar must be added to the food. It is added and so reaches the intestines in an already prepared state, while otherwise the intestines would make it themselves. The intestines make sugar from starch. That takes some doing.

Now another thing. Some people with weak stomachs can only digest soft-boiled eggs and not hard-boiled eggs. And once they have started to smell a bit it is even worse! Albumen is a good food but if it gets into the intestines in a living state it would go bad and stink and be useless within us. We cannot tolerate albumen in the intestines in the state in which it is outside. It must be changed and above all, it must be dissolved. If you put it into water it does not dissolve. It needs something different. Trypsin dissolves it particularly well. So protein changes into liquid protein and while this happens something else is created in the human organism.

Through the action of the pancreatic juices something else is created. It sounds very amusing, but alcohol is created. Man makes alcohol in his body. One does not have to drink alcohol, one has one's own source. Alcohol is made in the intestines. When a man takes to drink it is because his liver is too greedy. It is not enough for it to perceive the alcohol being made in the intestines, it wants more and the person becomes a drinker.

You see, people who knew this made it an excuse for wine and beer drinking. They said: Some people call themselves teetotallers, but nobody can be a teetotaller, because we make our own alcohol in our intestines! Well, this is of course no reason to drink a lot of alcohol and become addicted. Because if one gives in to the greed of the liver and drinks a lot of alcohol it becomes ill, it degenerates and becomes enlarged. The liver has got to be active. When it becomes enlarged the small glands become inflated. And when it should work to produce gall it does not produce proper gall. The chyme is not properly mixed with gall and it is an abnormal chyme that gets into the lymph vessels and the blood. This reaches the heart and affects it. Therefore people who drink a lot of beer have a liver that is sick and looks quite different from the liver of those who drink little or make do with the alcohol produced in their own intestines, which is, on the whole, enough. A degenerated liver and heart are the direct result of too much alcohol, hence the 'beer heart' which is very prevalent among the people of Munich, but the liver is always affected at the same time. So you see, one understands degeneration and various diseases if one looks in this way at the different processes involved in the passage of food through the organism.

Now I have told you what happens when protein dissolves. Alcohol penetrates the protein and prevents it going bad and stinking. You know if one wants to preserve living tissue one puts it in alcohol because alcohol preserves it. It keeps. Protein does not go bad in the organism because the organism itself puts it in alcohol. This is extraordinarily clever.

But all these processes which take place are so subtle that we would not be capable of reproducing them. We can do it to a certain extent. If we want to preserve a part of the human body or a small organism we put it in spirit and place it on the shelf. But in a much more subtle and intelligent way, trypsin does this in the human intestine. It produces alcohol and puts the protein into it.

And what happens to the fats? Well, they also go into the intestines and are transformed by the pancreatic juices. The result is two substances. One of them is glycerine. You are familiar with glycerine outside of your body, but you produce it daily within it. The other substance is an acid. Fats are converted into glycerine and acids — all kinds of fatty acids.

Only the salts remain almost unchanged. At the most they are dissolved so that they are easily digestible, but they remain almost as they are. Salts remain salts.

Starch : sugar
Protein: liquid protein
Fats   : glycerine, acids
Salts   : salts

So you see in various foods we eat starch-like substances, protein-like substances, fat-like substances and salts, and after we have digested them we have within us instead — sugar, liquid protein, glycerine and acids and salts.

And what happens to all this inside us? It is something quite different from what we have eaten. We have completely transformed everything.

Some centuries ago, here in Switzerland — but he travelled widely — there was a doctor, rather scorned by modern

18

science, who still had some ideas concerning these processes. This was Paracelsus. He was a professor in Basle but they threw him out because he knew more than all the others. Even today he is still universally maligned. Now although he was a very sensible and able man, it happened one day that he fell from a precipitous path and cracked his head. He had spent his last years in Salzburg. He was a doctor. Had he been a worthy citizen, a town counsellor for instance, he would have been greatly esteemed and lived on in people's memory. But he was a man who knew more than the others and so they said he was drunk and fell over the edge of the rock — this is how things are in this world. He had still known something and spoke with conviction about the powers of transformation in the human body, but in the course of centuries all this had been forgotten.

And now what happens to all this inside us? Here again science is deluded, for it says that all the sugar, liquid protein, alcohol, glycerine, fatty acids and salts pass into the blood vessels and from there to the heart, and from the heart via the blood vessels into the rest of the organism.

True, with the thickest of the fluid — everything is liquid but some is thicker than the rest — it can be so, it is so. It passes into the blood vessels and supplies the rest of the body. But have you ever found if you have a glass of water and put sugar in and drink it, that it is only sweet at the bottom where the sugar was? The whole glass of water is sweet, is it not? Sugar when dissolved distributes itself evenly in the water. Salt likewise. In this glass of water there are no blood vessels to take the sugar or salt into all its parts, instead the water sucks it up.

Now I have told you that man consists of 90% water, or at least of fluid. It is living water, but it is water. Do all the substances need the blood vessels to penetrate the whole of the body? When sugar is made in the intestines, does it need blood vessels in order to find its way into the whole of the body? Man consists of water so that sugar can spread through him.

People say if somebody is a confirmed drinker that all the alcohol that he drinks goes via the intestines to the heart and from there into the rest of the body. I can assure you, gentlemen, that if all the alcohol drunk by such an alcoholic would have to go through the heart it would not take years to finish him off but only days. One can establish the fact that liquids taken into the body do not go through the blood vessels into the rest of the body but penetrate the body like sugar does a glass of water. If someone with a reasonably good constitution drinks a glass of water when he is thirsty, the first glass of water is actually taken up by the intestine and mixed with the chyme and from there really does make its way via the blood vessels to the heart and so into the body. But once the blood vessels and the heart have got enough, you can drink as much water as you like, it does not go through the blood vessels because it is no longer needed. If you drink one glass or a glass and a half of water, just enough to quench your thirst, then your body will not be burdened, but if you drink too much, already the third or fourth glass passes quickly into the urine. It has not the time to pass through the heart, but because man is a column of water and it would add too much water, it passes out through the urine. Think what happens when people sit at the bar and reach the third or fourth glass of beer; first one and then another has to go outside. This beer has not taken the time to go to the heart. It has taken a much shorter route out, because man is a fluid body.

So we can say the chyme which consists of sugar, liquid protein, glycerine, acids and salts goes straight into the whole body. Only the thickest part of it goes via the blood vessels. And so it comes about that salts are deposited in the head and all the other organs, not via the blood, but directly.

Now you see, if we were to feel all the salts which are deposited in our head, we would have a continual headache. Too many salts in the head causes headache. You have

20

probably heard of migraine. I have already mentioned it here. On different levels one can explain things in different ways. What is migraine? It comes about when this process of distribution is not in order and too many salts, i.e. uric acid salts, are deposited in the head. Instead of the uric acid salts passing out in the urine, they remain in the head, because the other foodstuffs are not properly prepared and retain the salts within them. Migraine is not such an aristocratic disease, though it is prevalent among the gentry. Migraine is an undignified disease. What should be excreted with the urine is deposited on the right side of the head, because it went bad in the stomach. What takes place in the left side of the body affects the right side of the head. I will explain another time why this is so.

And so it happens that what should be excreted through the urine is deposited in the right side of the head.

How much salt can man bear? Now remember what I once told you. Remember I said that in the head is the brain fluid and only because of this is the weight of the brain so reduced that we can sustain it. A body in air has a certain gravity, a certain weight, but when we immerse it in water it becomes lighter. If this were not so, we could not swim. The brain, if it were not in a fluid, would weigh about 1,500 grams. But because it floats in a liquid, it weighs only 20 grams. It becomes that much lighter. It weighs only 20 grams. But the more salts there are deposited in the brain, the heavier it becomes because the salts increase the weight of the brain. It simply becomes too heavy.

Now of course we can say that when man deposits salts in the brain, that the salts also become lighter, that the whole thing becomes lighter because of buoyancy. But now imagine how different everything is in man compared with the animal. Man has planted his head on top of the rest of his organism. Thus the head has a substantial support. With the animal this is different. Its head has no support. It sticks out in front. What is the result? In man the pressure of the head,

21

although it is quite light, is held by the body. Not so in the animal. This is the main difference between man and animal.

Scientists are always trying to think how man has developed from the animal. Of course it is very good to think, but one cannot look at man in this way. One cannot say: The animal has so many bones and man has an equal number. The ape has so many bones and man has an equal number, therefore it is all the same. One cannot say this. You cannot deny that the head of the ape hangs forward however upright it walks, even if it is an orang-outang or a gorilla. Man is so built that his head rests on his body and the pressure is absorbed by the body. What happens?

Something very remarkable happens. We have within us sugar, liquid protein, glycerine, acids and salts. The salts go from the abdomen up to the head and are deposited there. They must go back again, and they go back through the body if there are too many of them. With regard to the other substances, something else has to happen in the body. While they go up, a new transformation takes place, because the body holds back the gravity. A part of the substances becomes lighter and lighter. Another part — the thicker — is deposited. If one dissolves something there can remain a deposit at the bottom, likewise all the way between abdomen and head deposits are formed. But the lighter parts go on up and are transformed by this diminished gravity. What arises if those parts of the food which are *not* the lightest parts go to the head and are transformed? There arises a kind of phosphorus. This is a fact. Out of the food arises a kind of phosphorus so that the food itself does not reach the head. A good deal reaches the head — sugar, glycerine, and so on — all kinds of things go up, but a part is transformed into phosphorus before it arrives.

So we have salts in the head which come from the outside world in an almost untransformed state. Then there is phosphorus, very finely dispersed, very much finer than air. These are the main substances in the head — salts and phosphorus. The others are only there to enable man to support himself as a living being. But the most important are salts and phosphorus.

One can prove, as I will show you another time, that if a man has not got the right amount of salts in the head, he cannot think properly. One must have the right amount of salts in the head in order to think properly. Salt in the head serves our faculty of thinking. This is in addition to what I have already told you about thinking. Things in man are very complicated.

If we have too much phosphorus in us from eating too hot and spicy food, then we become terrible fidgets who want to put their fingers into everything, we are full of the will to do things. We have 'will' through the presence of phosphorus, and if we have too much, the will begins to get restless. And if the organism is so constituted that it always sends too much phosphorus into the head, then a person does not only fidget and become nervous and restless (which has nothing to do with nerves but with phosphorus) but he begins to rave, becomes a madman, a raving maniac. We must have a little bit of phosphorus in us so that we can have a will, but if we make too much ourselves, we become mad.

$$\text{Head} \begin{cases} \text{salt} & : \text{thinking} \\ \\ \text{phosphorus:} & \text{will} \end{cases}$$

Now think of this. If somebody gives you salt, how do you make it think? (I would like to recommend you to take a salt cellar and try to make it think!) *You* do it constantly. Inside your head you constantly use salt for thinking. And then rub off a little phosphorus from a match and light it and try to burn it. Now it should exert will. It will burn but it will not exert will. But *you* do this constantly inside you. And now don't you think that there is something in you that is far cleverer than your stupid head, which is so incapable

23

that it cannot make a thinking being out of salt nor a being of will out of phosphorus? What *can* do it is what we call the soul/spiritual within us. It is this living, interweaving element that is the soul/spiritual in us. This is planted in us, it makes use of the salt in the head to think and makes use of the phosphorus which goes up like finest smoke and gives us will.

So from the body one is led to the soul and spirit if one looks at things rightly. But what does modern science do? It stops at the belly. At the most it knows that sugar, etc. arises in the abdomen. After this it loses all trace of how things proceed. It does not know what happens, therefore it cannot say anything about soul and spirit. This science must be supplemented and extended. One must not limit oneself to the abdomen and only consider the head as stuck on top. One does not see what rises up. One thinks things happen the same way in the head as in the belly. The whole thing is due to the fact that modern science only knows something about the abdomen. It only knows that something arises there, but it does not know that the liver perceives and the kidneys think. It does not know it for the simple reason that it knows nothing of what is in the head. It does not look for anything there because it takes the liver lying on the dissecting table as the whole. But it is not the whole, because it has lost the soul by the time it was in a condition to be dissected. As long as the soul is within it, it cannot be cut out of the body. So you see that a serious responsible science must continue to work where modern science is obliged to stop. This is the heart of the matter. This is why we have built the Goetheanum, so that science shall not only know something incomplete about the abdomen, but will be able to explain something about the whole body. Then it will be a real science.

5

THE EFFECT OF ALCOHOL

Extract from a
Lecture to the Workmen   Dornach, 8th January 1923

You want to know to what extent alcohol is harmful to health. Well, the first effect of alcohol is immediately visible, in fact quite obvious, because it acts in man on what we have been talking about so much, on his whole soul condition. To begin with he gets into a state of mental confusion. He is subject to emotions which when he is sober are weak enough to be quite easily controlled, so that when he has not taken alcohol he appears more reasonable than when he has. Alcohol also fires the blood, and the circulation is accelerated. In this way the emotional life is stirred up. For instance a person flies into a temper much more easily, while at other times he can more readily control it. So you see the first effect of alcohol is directed against man's reason and his soul life in general.

When alcohol has been in the organism for some time the result is something with which you are quite familiar — a hangover. From the way a hangover arises you can see that the immediate effect of alcohol causes the organism to revolt against it. What is a hangover really? It means that the person who was drunk, let us say in the evening (hangovers usually occur the morning after) thus causing his blood to move too fast, used up a lot of energy because of the general acceleration of movement in the body which otherwise would have been much slower.

Now get this quite clear. Assume that the body is set to do a certain amount of work in twenty-four hours. If somebody drinks a drop too much, the same work will be done within

25

twelve hours or even six. In this way the body deprives itself of work it might be doing. People who are in the habit of drinking a bit too much now and then, quite instinctively eat a good meal afterwards, before the hangover sets in. Why do they do it? If they eat well afterwards the hangover is either quite averted or at least so reduced that they can work the next day. What happens when someone, shall we say, who has obviously drunk too much, follows it up with a plate of sausages? Then he sets his body to work again and replaces what was used up by the accelerated activity. If however a person does *not* do this (if he is not a hardened drinker — for they always do it) if he forgets to eat the sausages he gets a hangover because then his body is not in a position to maintain a heightened inner activity. If this work is not properly carried through, waste products are deposited, mainly products of uric acid. They are deposited principally in the head because it is the most difficult to protect. And so a person who has used up the inner activity of his body during the night through drinking alcohol, walks about the next morning with a head in the condition of his intestines — waste products are deposited in it. The body revolts at once when too much activity is demanded of it through the intake of alcohol.

Now as I have said before in these lectures, man can stand much more than is usually supposed, not only as regards alcohol, but in general. For a long time the balance can be repeatedly restored. There is a very deceptive and suspect antidote against hangovers used by some when they find themselves with a terrible head the next morning or when they come home — they drink more. I am sure you know this, the next morning they drink more — they make morning drinking into a remedial treatment.

What does this further drinking do? During the night the body had been deprived of activity because the blood had been unduly agitated. In the morning this activity is lacking. Now the body is spurred on by the renewed drinking and the last remains of possible activity are used up. This final activity removes the waste products, and the hangover, to a certain extent, goes out of the head, but remains all the more in the rest of the body. But people feel this less. Drinking in the morning after a hangover transfers it to the rest of the body where it remains unconscious, and only when this happens does the body get into real trouble. Those alcoholics who drive away hangovers with further drinking are in the worst plight, for when this is repeated time and again the whole body will gradually be wrecked.

But because man can stand such a lot, it is almost impossible to wreck the body so easily. The real alcoholic first gets into a delirium, a drunken madness. At this stage the damage is not final, for when this delirium tremens — as it is called — sets in, you can see that the body is still putting up a defense. When delirium tremens sets in people get a sort of persecution mania. They see themselves surrounded by all sorts of little animals, mice, etc. It is a characteristic of delirium tremens that people feel they are pursued by little animals, mice in particular. This has even come down in history. There are towers called 'mouse towers'.* They usually got their name from the fact that someone was once locked up in them who was mad drunk and was plagued by imaginary mice (there were probably some real ones there too) but the person inside saw himself surrounded everywhere by thousands and thousands of mice which were not there.

You see, that which ruins man when he drinks is actually quite difficult to get into his body. The body resists for a long time what alcohol does to it.

An interesting thing is that when people are pricked by their conscience — say they have been drinking heavily for a time, also in the morning — their conscience stirs and they stop drinking. They have still just enough strength left to

* There is one near Bingen on the Rhine (translator's note).

stop drinking. What happens now? If they have not had delirium tremens before, they get it now. This is the interesting fact. Those who have been drinking for a long time and then stop, often get this delirium.

This is one of the most important signs which show that one must realise that the functions of the head are different from those of the rest of the body — as I have told you in recent lectures. As long as a person keeps the after-effects of his intoxication in his head, things are still tolerable, they have not yet entered the rest of the body. Once they have done so and then he gives up alcohol, the rest of the body revolts violently and the head suffers from it. Then the person gets delirium tremens from giving up drinking. When he no longer gets the stimulus, the delirium overtakes him.

One can say the human blood is the bodily counterpart of the most important faculties of the soul. Perhaps you know that some people suffer from persecution mania. They see all kinds of things which are not really there. In former times one used to bleed them and it was a very good cure. People were not so superstitious in those days as one assumes they were. Bleeding did not derive from superstition. People were bled usually by applying leeches somewhere which sucked their blood. The power of the blood is then less effective. In acute attacks of madness, but not actually in the case of drunkenness, the power of the blood was reduced and their condition improved.

I have spoken to you previously about something which has very little relation to all this — the nervous system, as the foundation of the characteristics of man's soul. The nervous system is less important for the will. It is important for the intellect, but is far less important for the human will than the blood.

When you see how greatly alcohol affects the blood, you can realise that because the body revolts so violently against what alcohol does, the blood is well protected. The blood is really extraordinarily well protected against what alcohol does, against the attacks of alcohol in man. So we must ask: What is it that protects the blood so extraordinarily well against these attacks? Further, we must ask: Where do the most important things in the blood have their origin?

You remember I told you that blood consists of red corpuscles which swim about in the blood serum, as it is called. It also consists of white corpuscles. These are the most important constituents of the blood — red and white corpuscles. We are not talking about the corpuscles connected with the spleen which we have called regulators in our experiments in Stuttgart. There are of course many different corpuscles in the blood. We will now only concern ourselves with the red and white corpuscles and ask: Where in the body do they originate? You see, they come into existence in a very special place: When you think of a thigh bone — between hip and knee — or another bone, an arm bone for instance — any bone as long as it is hollow — you will find that it is filled with bone marrow. In this marrow the red and white blood corpuscles are born and from there make their way into the blood vessels. The human body is so organised that its blood — the most important thing in it — is created in the inner cavities of its bones.

Since this is so it is clear that where it is created the blood is extraordinarily well protected against ruination. The alcohol must have been drunk excessively and for a long time if it is to destroy the bone and get right into the marrow and destroy it so that no red and white corpuscles are produced any more. It is really the fatal point for the alcoholic when alcohol works into the bone marrow.

With regard to their intellect — the characteristics of the soul — people are somewhat similar, but as regards their blood, the sexes, male and female, are very different. It is an unconscious difference which however is very evident. What is created in the interior of the bone — the blood corpuscles — of these, the red ones are more important in the woman and the white in the man. This is very important:

the red corpuscles are more important in the woman, the white in the man.

As you know, every four weeks the woman has her period which is fundamentally a process of excretion to get rid of those red blood corpuscles that need to be cast out. The man has no periods and you can see that semen is not derived from red corpuscles. It is derived from the white ones. They go through many changes but in the end they become the most important thing in the semen. So if we want to find out what can influence physically human reproduction, we must go back to the well-protected bone marrow. Human reproduction can be influenced physically via the marrow within the bones.

Now, of course, when the red and white corpuscles have been produced in the bones, they pass into the blood. If the woman drinks it is mainly the red corpuscles that are influenced. They contain iron, are slightly heavy, having earthly gravity in them. If the woman drinks, she brings it about that there is too much heaviness in her. The result is that the developing child becomes too heavy and therefore cannot form its organs properly. It develops but its inner organs are not in order. The damaging influence of alcohol penetrates into the inner organs through the woman.

If the man drinks, it is mainly the white corpuscles which are affected, and if fertilisation takes place under the influence of alcohol or under chronic alcoholism, one has to reckon with the fact that the sperm is so damaged that it becomes fidgety. In the process of fertilisation the little ovum is detached within the maternal organism. In this condition one can only see it with a microscope. So the ovum is detached. From the man a great number of sperms are detached. They all have tails. Innumerable sperms are contained in the seminal fluid. The tail is like a fine hair and with this fine hair they are anyway terribly restless. They make the most complicated movements and obviously one of them must reach the female ovum first, and this one is taken into the

30

ovum. It is much smaller than the female egg. Though the ovum can only be seen with the aid of a microscope, the male sperm is even smaller. It enters. The moment it has entered, a skin forms round the ovum and all the later comers are repulsed by it. Only one can enter. As soon as it is inside, a skin is formed round the ovum and the others must retreat.

You see it is extremely ingeniously arranged. These little sperm creatures are extraordinarily lively anyway and with alcohol they become really fidgety so that fertilisation takes place influenced by male sperm which are abnormally mobile. The result is that the system of the nerves and senses are affected when the man drinks. So when the woman drinks the inner organs will be damaged through weight, when the man drinks the nervous system of the child will be damaged. All that takes place in the developing child will be ruined instead of taking its normal course.

So one can say: When the woman drinks, the terrestrial element is damaged. When the man drinks, it is the airy and movable elements encompassing the earth, which man also carries within him, which are damaged. So that from both sides the offspring will be damaged if both drink. Of course, the fertilisation can hardly be normal, i.e. fertilisation is possible, but not really the proper growth of the offspring. On the one hand the ovum wants to assert its weightiness and on the other hand everything is in fidgety movement and each contradicts the other. The male contradicts the female in such a fertilisation, when both drink. So if one understands how all this hangs together then it is clear that habitual drinking is extremely damaging to the offspring. People, however, do not believe it because the influence of drink both in men and women is relatively not so very obvious. But this is only so, because the blood is well protected, being created in the marrow, and people have to do a lot if they would greatly influence their offspring. Slight influences people are not prepared to admit.

If a child is born with hydrocephalus one does not usually ascertain whether conception took place during a night after the mother had been out to a good dinner with red wine to drink. One would find if one were to investigate that the child was born with hydrocephalus because gravity (weight) became too strong. If on the other hand a child is born with a facial, muscular twitch, one does not usually ascertain whether the man drank too much the evening before fertilisation took place. The smaller things, I would say, are not taken into account, and people then think there is no influence. There always is. However, the really damaging influences are the outcome of habitual drinking. And here again we have something remarkable and rather strange.

You see when the man drinks it can happen that the nervous system of the children is weakened and they may have for instance a tendency to consumption. What is hereditary in the children, however, need not be connected with the father's drinking. For instance, they need not have a tendency to mental disturbance, it can also be consumption, or stomach upsets or suchlike. This is what is so treacherous about alcohol: the evil done by it can simply pass over into other organs. . . .

Quite insignificant damaging influences can eventually lead to the undermining of the health and whole inner organisation of man.

Man can stand a lot, but from a certain moment the organism refuses to function. As regards drinking, the organism goes on strike from the moment that alcohol prevents life functions, the invisible life functions, from working in the right way.

When man drinks too much alcohol, and goes on and on drinking, so that the alcoholism is not acute but becomes chronic as they say, it comes to the point when alcohol acts on man directly as alcohol.

How does it work as alcohol? Now I would remind you that I told you that man creates for himself the amount of

32

alcohol he needs. I told you that in the contents of the intestines a certain amount of alcohol is always needed. Why is it needed? You need only remember, if you have ever seen anatomical exhibits, that they were kept in alcohol, otherwise they would decompose. Alcohol prevents the rotting of what comes from the living body. The alcohol which the human body itself produces, acts in the same way. It prevents the decomposition of substances which are needed by man. Man's inner organisation prescribes how much alcohol it should have, because he has in his body certain substances which he needs and which would go bad if they were not preserved.

But now supposing someone drinks too much alcohol, then too much will be preserved. What should be expelled from the body is retained. If he exposes the blood circulating in the body to alcohol time and time again, this blood will be preserved in the body. What is the result? It is that the blood blocks the canals in the bones. It is not expelled quickly enough, it remains too long in the body, the marrow is not encouraged to form new blood and so becomes weak. And what happens with chronic alcoholics is that in time the bone marrow becomes weak. Then in the woman the normal red corpuscles are not produced, nor the white corpuscles in the man.

Now when one speaks about such things I have to say: It is all very well for people to have ideas on social reform — for instance prohibition and so on. Certainly it is very nice. But look at it this way. Even such a learned man as Professor Benedikt — about whom I once told you that he collected the skulls of criminals, and then the Hungarian criminals said that they would not have their skulls sent to Vienna because then they would not be able to join up with the rest of their bones on the Day of Judgement — this man quite rightly said: Alright, people hold forth against alcohol, but many more people die of water than of alcohol! Of course this is true in general, for if water is contaminated, the effect is soon widely noticeable. Merely statistically one can say that more people die of water than of alcohol....

But we must look at it differently. One must notice that alcohol gradually works its way into the marrow and gradually ruins the blood. So, by damaging the offspring, the whole subsequent progeny is damaged. If a person has, let us say, three children, these children are somewhat damaged, but their offspring will be considerably damaged. And so people are ruined far into the future through alcohol. Many of the weaknesses afflicting mankind today are due to the fact that our ancestors drank too much. Now really imagine: Here is a man and a woman. The man drinks. The bodies of the offspring are weakened. Now think what this means after just one century, or even more so, after several centuries. It is no good selecting a period — say from 1870 to 1880 — and saying that more people died of water than of alcohol. One must spread one's gaze over longer periods. And this is just what people today do not like to do....

If one thinks in terms of social welfare one must have thoughts that go beyond immediate concerns. Now I must say that to my thinking it is like this: Forbid — of course one can prohibit alcohol, but you see, very strange things can then happen. You know for instance that in many parts of the world people began to restrict the sale of alcohol or even forbid it, but I would draw your attention to the mischief that has crept into Europe recently — cocaine, which people take to become intoxicated. Alcohol is gold in comparison to cocaine and what it does mainly as damage to human reproduction. There will be one or another who will not consider it irresponsible to take cocaine. But even from the outer symptoms you can see how much worse cocaine is than alcohol. If a person has delirium tremens from alcohol he gets persecution mania. He sees mice everywhere which persecute him. If, however, someone takes cocaine, snakes come out of his body everywhere. When such a person becomes intoxicated by cocaine, it is very pleasant at first.

Cocaine produces a certain sense of well-being. But then, after a time, when he looks at himself, he sees that he looks like this (a drawing was made), snakes are coming out of his body everywhere and he rushes back to take more cocaine to keep the snakes at bay for a while. His fear of the snakes is much greater than the alcoholic's fear of mice in delirium tremens.

One can of course prohibit this and that, but then people think of something else which is usually not much better, in fact probably worse. I really believe that explaining and making clear how alcohol works in the way we have done today, will be more effective and make people gradually give up alcohol of their own accord. It does not infringe on human freedom but people will say by themselves: 'This is really alarming. I will be ruined right into the bones.' This works on the feelings, while laws work through the intellect. Real truths and real knowledge are those which work into the feelings. Therefore it is my conviction that we shall only achieve an effective social reform — for it is very similar in other realms — when we spread enlightenment in the widest possible circles. . . .

What one can learn about alcohol can be understood by everyone. And now we come to what I always say. People come and ask: Is it better not to drink alcohol or to drink alcohol? Is it better to be a vegetarian or to eat meat? I never tell anyone whether he should give up alcohol or drink it, whether he should eat plants or meat. I say to people: Alcohol does so and so. I simply explain its effect, and then they may decide whether to drink or not. I do the same with regard to vegetarian or meat diet: Meat does this and plants do that. And the result is that they can decide for themselves.

That is what one must have above all in science — respect for human freedom. One should never have the feeling that anyone is ordered or forbidden to do something; instead one tells him the facts. What he will do when he knows how alcohol works is his own affair. What is right to do he then finds out of himself. In this way we will get somewhere. In this way free men will be able to direct themselves. This must be our aim. This is the way to real social reform.

6

THE EFFECTS OF NICOTINE.
VEGETARIAN AND MEAT DIETS. ABSINTH

Extracts from a
Lecture to the Workmen   Dornach, 13th January 1923

Questions were asked on the effects of nicotine and of vegetarian and meat diets and absinth.

Rudolf Steiner: We will try to go into these questions. One request was to speak about nicotine, that is the poison which is introduced into the body by smoking and any other use of tobacco. You see, we must be clear about what are the effects of nicotine. Its effect is above all on the heart. It increases its activity. Now since the heart itself is not a pump but only indicates what is going on in the body (the heart beats faster when the blood circulates faster) this means that nicotine really affects the circulation of the blood and makes it more lively. One must have this quite clear: The introduction of nicotine into the human body enlivens the circulation of the blood and this increases the activity of the heart.

Now we must pursue further these processes in the human organism and keep in mind that everything that takes place in the organism is strictly ordered and regulated. For instance one can hardly imagine anything more important for the human body than the fact that the pulse of an adult or even an older person is approximately 72 per minute.

On the other hand — as I have told you before — man takes about 18 breaths per minute. If you multiply 18 by 4 you get 72. This means that on an average, the pulse beats four times as fast as the breathing. Naturally this is only an average, for it varies with every person. This variation is just what makes people different. But the average is 1 to 4, i.e. the blood rhythm is 4 times as fast as that of the breath.

Now if I introduce nicotine into the human organism, I can introduce it for two reasons. I can do it out of a craving for tobacco, or as a remedy. Everything that is a poison, is also a remedy. One can say that everything is poison and remedy. Obviously if you drink several buckets of water straight off, it would be a poison, while water taken in normal quantities is nourishment and if it is taken in minute quantities it can even be a remedy. Altogether water is a very effective remedy, used in all kinds of ways. So, even of common substances one can say that what is poison can also be remedy. And therefore one must know how a substance works on the human organism.

Thus if I introduce tobacco into the body, the blood circulation is stimulated. The blood becomes more lively and circulates more quickly. The breathing however is not quickened to the same degree. The rate of breathing remains the same. Consequently the circulation and the breathing no longer correspond as they did before. For instance, if we take an average person (such a person does not exist but we assume he does) he should take 18 breaths and have a pulse of 72 per minute. Through taking nicotine he has now a pulse of — shall we say — 76. Now he no longer has a correct relationship between pulse and breathing.

The result of this is that, since with every pulse beat a certain quantity of oxygen should combine with the blood, the blood no longer receives sufficient oxygen. The result of nicotine poisoning is therefore that too much oxygen is demanded by the blood. The indrawn breath does not supply it. The consequence is a very slight shortness of breath. This is so slight that it is not recognised as such, for as I have told you, the human body can stand a lot. Nevertheless taking nicotine always causes a definite slight shortness of breath. This very slight shortness of breath causes a feeling of distress with every intake of breath. Every shortage of

38

breath causes a feeling of slight anxiety. If you are afraid, and you carry this fear around with you, you can more easily control it than this extremely small anxiety which remains quite unconscious. The deeper causes of illness are just such very slight fears which remain unnoticed. The incessant smoker is continually exposed to these causes — he is always, without knowing it, completely filled with a certain anxiety. You know that when you are afraid your heart beats faster. This shows you that some one who is continually poisoning himself with nicotine has always a heartbeat that is too fast. But if the heart works a bit too fast it will thicken just as my biceps will develop and thicken if I regularly exercise them. Well, of course, under certain circumstances this is not so bad if it does not result in a torn muscle. But once the heart, which is also a muscle, becomes too thick, it presses against the other organs. And the result is, as a rule, that through the fault of the heart the circulation is further disturbed. The circulation is not initiated by the heart but it can be disturbed if it finds a thickened heart.

Now when the heart becomes thickened, the next thing is that the kidneys become affected, because through the harmonious working of heart and kidneys the whole organisation of the human body is kept in order. Heart and kidneys must always be in tune. Of course, everything in man must work in harmony, but heart and kidneys are in immediate connection with each other. One notices at once if anything is wrong with the heart; the kidneys then are also no longer quite in order and it follows that excretion is not as it should be. An alien influence affects the excretion of urine and as a result the life tempo of a person is considerably speeded up, leading to a good deal more wear and tear. And so he who gets more nicotine into his body than is good for his constitution, will gradually destroy himself. He is really ruined by all kinds of states of inner anxieties affecting the heart.

It is really quite easy to recognise the influence of states of

39

anxiety on the faculties of the soul. It is noticeable that in the case of people who take in too much nicotine the power of thought is gradually adversely affected. It is influenced because a person who goes about in a state of slight fear cannot think properly. Thus one can generally recognise nicotine poisoning in people by the fact that their thinking is also not quite in order. They form opinions far too quickly. These hasty judgements can be magnified even to the proportions of persecution mania. So one can say truly that enjoyment of nicotine, when it is an indulgence, undermines health.

But in all these things you must also look at the other side. You see smoking has only become a custom during the course of man's development. Originally man did not smoke. The enjoyment of tobacco only gradually took hold. Well, we must look at the other side. Imagine that we have the condition about which I have spoken. A man has for instance a pulse of only 68 instead of 72. His circulation is not quick enough and now he starts to smoke. The circulation will now be stimulated from 68 to 72 so that breathing and pulse will have the correct relationship. Therefore, if someone consults a doctor because he does not feel well in some way or other and the doctor finds his pulse too slow, he could even recommend smoking.

I have said that when the circulation is too fast in relation to the breath there occur those states of anxiety of which, however, one is not conscious. But if someone has too slow a pulse for some reason or other, he goes around wanting something but nobody knows what he wants. It is a symptom of illness when people wander around wanting something but not knowing what they want. Think how many people there are who go around like this, not knowing what they want! They are, as one says, discontented with life. There are people, are there not, who find that whatever profession they embrace it does not suit them, and so on. This is connected with too slow a circulation. In such a case one can say it is even good to introduce a little nicotine as a remedy. And if someone finds smoking pleasant, one does not have to give him nicotine as a medicine but can advise him to smoke — if he was a non-smoker before.

You see, it is a fact that nowadays there are more and more people who don't really know what they want. It is very easy in our days for people not to know what they want, for in the last three or four centuries the majority have given up taking any interest in spiritual matters. They go to their office, busy themselves with what they don't really like doing but which brings in money, and sit out their office hours. They may be quite industrious but have no real interests apart from going out to the theatre and reading the paper. Gradually it has come to this. For instance, it is rare today for anyone to read a book.

All this is because people do not really know what they want. They need to be told. When you read the papers or go out to the theatre it stimulates the senses and the intellect but does not stir the blood. If however one sits down to read a difficult book, the blood *is* stimulated. As soon as one has to make an effort to understand something the blood is stimulated. But this is what people do not like any more. They do not *want* to have to exert themselves to understand something. This goes against the grain. They do not want to understand anything. And through not wanting to understand, their blood becomes thick. The thick blood moves slower and the result is that they always need a remedy to get this ever thickening blood moving. It gets moving when they put that glowing weed — the stick of nicotine — in their mouths. But even then it does not get any thinner and the circulation becomes more and more difficult. The result can be that signs of ageing appear earlier than need be. From this one sees that the human body is extraordinarily sensitive in its processes. One does not only learn something by investigating the blood but also from the way a person behaves, whether he thinks slowly or quickly.

41

So you see, if someone wants to know about the effect of nicotine, he must know a lot about the whole circulatory and breathing system.

Now you remember what I explained to you in detail the other day. Blood is created in the bone marrow; that is where it comes from. So, if the blood, produced in the marrow, is made to circulate too fast then the marrow itself has to work faster. The result is that the bones cannot catch up with their work and then little organisms develop within the bones which gradually devour us during our life. There were doctors, Metschnikoff was one of them, who believed that these osteoclasts, as these little fellows are called, are the cause of human death. If there were no osteoclasts, said Metschnikoff, then we would live for ever. He thought that they really ate us up. It is actually a fact that the older we get the more osteoclasts there are. So it is true that our bones are gradually devoured. From another point of view it is as if a field was well manured. More then grows on it than if it is not well manured. And if one introduces something into the body such as nicotine, this means that for ourselves we injure the bones but for the osteoclasts — these man-eaters and consumers of bones — we could not prepare these bones better. What is bad for man is the very best thing one can do for these little creatures.

This is how it is in the world. If someone wants to be comfortable in his mind, he thinks that the world was created by the good God and everything in it is good. But one can say: Why did the good God allow the osteoclasts to grow alongside the bone marrow? If he had not allowed the osteoclasts to grow we would not be eaten up during our lifetime. We could so ill-treat our bones that they would eventually perish from other causes, but they would last anyway for centuries if these little beasts were not inside.

But it does not help if one just thinks comfortably. It only helps if one really goes into the facts and if one knows that the subtle forces taking part in the forming of bones have their enemies. These too are created, and they are the

42

osteoclasts which exist in their millions within us. The older you get the more osteoclasts you have. You always have man-eaters within you, even if they are only small. The cannibals — the large man-eaters — are not the most clever; the cleverest are the little ones we carry within us and which find good pasture when we introduce nicotine into the body.

From all this you can realise how extraordinarily important it is to understand thoroughly the human being as a whole if one wants to convey any idea of how any particular substance works in the human body.

Man is continually eating. He eats animal and vegetable substances. Now I have already told you that I would never dream of trying to persuade anyone to follow this or that diet. I merely state the effects. It has often happened that vegetarians have come to me and said that they sometimes tend to feel faint, etc. and I have to say to them: 'That comes from the fact that you don't eat any meat.' You see one must look at things objectively. One must not want to force anything. But what does it mean to 'look objectively' with regard to vegetarianism and meat eating? Well gentlemen, look at a plant. From its germinating seed which sends its root into the earth, the plant is able to bring forth green leaves and coloured petals. Now compare something you get from a plant — either you pick ears of corn or green leaves and make them into some sort of vegetable dish — compare it with meat, with the muscle of animals. It is quite a different substance, isn't it? What is the relation between these two substances? You know, there are animals which simply are good vegetarian creatures. They eat no meat. Take for instance our cows, they eat no meat, nor are horses very keen on it, for they too eat only plants. Now you see the animal does not only stuff itself with food, it also continually casts out that which is in its body. You know that birds moult. They lose their feathers and have to replace them with new ones. You know that stags cast their antlers. You yourselves cut your nails and they grow again. All this

43

is outwardly visible and it happens all the time. We are also continually shedding our skin. I have explained this to you once before. Within seven or eight years we shed our whole body and replace it by a new one. It is the same with animals. Take a cow or an ox. When you look at them again after a few years, the flesh they are made of is quite other than it was. With cattle it is a little different from man. It goes quicker. So there is a renewal of the flesh. Out of what has it been made? From nothing but plant substance! The cow herself in her own body has produced flesh from plant material. The important point is that the animal body is able to produce flesh from plant material.

Gentlemen, you can cook your cabbage as long as you like, it will not turn into meat! Never will you get meat in your pan or pot. Nor has anybody ever baked a cake that has turned into meat. One cannot make meat artificially. But in the animal body there is manufactured what cannot be made artificially. Meat is produced in the animal body. But the forces to do this must be in the body. Among our technical means there are no forces capable of making meat out of plants. We have not got them. However, in our body and in the animal body there *are* forces which can make meat substance out of plant substance.

Now look at a plant. This is a plant (a drawing is made on the board). There it is in the meadow or in the field. Up to this point its forces have been active, have produced green leaves, berries and so on. Now imagine a cow goes and eats this plant. When the cow eats this plant it turns it into meat. This means the cow has the forces which enable it internally to transform this plant into meat.

Now imagine this cow would take it into her head to say: It is so boring for me to have to wander around here and tear off these plants. I can let another animal do it for me, and then I will eat that animal. Fine! The cow would then begin to eat meat. Yet she herself is able to produce meat. She has the necessary forces. What happens when instead of

44

eating plants she goes straight for the meat? All the forces which could produce meat are left idle. Imagine if you had a factory somewhere which should be producing something and then you produce nothing but the machinery goes on running. What a waste of energy! A tremendous lot of energy is lost. Yes, but the energy which is lost in the animal body cannot simply get lost. In the end the cow is completely filled up with this force which, instead of making meat out of plants, goes on and does something different. The force remains with her, it is there. It does something different in her. And what it does is to produce all kinds of waste products. Instead of meat, harmful substances are created. If the cow should suddenly become a meat-eater, she would be filled with harmful substances — mainly with uric acid and its salts.

Now these salts of uric acid have their own special habits. They have a liking for the nervous system and the brain. And if the cow were to eat meat, enormous quantities of uric acid salts would be deposited; they would go to the brain and the cow would become deranged. If we could make the experiment of suddenly feeding a herd of cows on pigeons, the result would be a completely mad herd. This is how it is. In spite of the gentleness of the doves the cows would become mad.

You see, such a thing disproves materialism, for if cattle ate only pigeons, they should become as gentle as doves if the material substance only were the active influence. However, they do most certainly not become gentle doves but they would become terribly violent raging beasts. This is borne out by the fact that horses become wild when they are given even a very little meat, they become wild straight away, because they too are not used to eating meat.

Obviously something of the same sort can be seen in man. Historically it is very interesting. One part of the population of Asia is strictly vegetarian. They are gentle people who do not often go to war. Only in western Asia did man begin to eat meat and there wars began to rage. So we see the Asiatic peoples who do not eat meat use the forces, which would otherwise be left idle, to transform plant substance into flesh. The result is they remain gentle, while the other peoples who eat meat do not remain so gentle.

Well of course mankind only gradually acquired the maturity to reflect on all this as we have been doing. When man began to eat meat he was not able to follow such thoughts as we have done. Everything arose from feeling and instinct.

You see the lion always eats meat. He is no herbivore. The lion has very short intestines. Herbivorous animals have very long intestines. So it is with man. If he is born into a people or race where all his forefathers have eaten meat, he will have a shorter intestine. It will have become shorter, too short for a pure vegetarian. And then he will have to do everything he can to maintain his health if he eats only plants.

Certainly, it is quite possible today to be a vegetarian and there is much to be said for it. There is a certain advantage in eating only plants, not meat. One does not tire so quickly. From within the organism one does not get so tired because one does not deposit all this uric acid and its salts. One does not tire so quickly and keeps a clearer head and can therefore think more easily, that is, if one thinks at all. For someone who does not think, there is no point in keeping his head free of uric acid salts, for it is of course necessary that the whole human organisation be in harmony. It is possible today for man to overcome himself and become a plant eater. Then he makes use of the forces which most people, because they eat meat, leave unused.

I will draw your attention to something rather peculiar. It is this. If today you look around the world perceptively you will find that there is an illness that can quickly undermine a person's health. It is known as diabetes. The first symptom is that sugar is found in the urine. And through

46

excessive production of sugar the body is soon destroyed. This illness puts us in a bit of a cleft stick. Sugar is the substance which inwardly supports us if it is rightly conveyed into the body. This can even be established statistically. In Russia there is far less sugar eaten than in England and this is what makes just the difference between the Russian and English races. The English have self-awareness and are egoistic; the Russians are a little weak, not egoistic, but weak. This is because in Russia little sugar is eaten while in England very much is eaten in food. The human body however needs a considerable quantity of sugar which it must work on and assimilate. In the same way as the bones support us, so do the quantities of sugar which are swirling around in our body support us. If however too much sugar goes into the urine, then too little goes into the body and the health will be ruined. This is diabetes.

Now it is a fact that today diabetes is more prevalent with Jews than with non-Jews. Of course, other people also have diabetes but today it is particularly frequent among Jews. The race has a tendency towards diabetes. Jews have a certain difficulty in assimilating sugar, on the other hand they need it. Therefore the Jewish diet should be such that it helps the body as much as possible to make use of sugar and not excrete it straight away.

When you read the Old Testament you will find all kinds of dietary regulations. These are still observed in restaurants displaying the notice 'Kosher'. You will know of such restaurants with 'Kosher' written in Hebrew lettering. There the cooking is Kosher. It is done according to the old Mosaic laws. And when you try to find what underlies these laws you will see that the Jew should, as far as possible, eat so that his body can cope with sugar, because this is a difficulty for the race. Above all the eating of pork was forbidden in order to prevent diabetes, since pig meat makes the proper utilisation of sugar particularly difficult for man. One should be able to read the Old Testament from a medical aspect;

47

this would be tremendously interesting. It is extraordinarily interesting to follow up the reasons for the various prohibitions and Kosher methods of cooking. Even the Jewish method of slaughter, for instance the way of killing poultry or other animals, is calculated to leave the correct amount of blood in the meat which the Jew eats, for the proper utilisation of sugar.

You will know that in recent times the Jews on the whole have become less strict in observing their dietary laws, yet, of course they remain their own race. The dietary commandments are racial laws and their non-observance is harmful. Thus the Jews contract diabetes more easily than other people. That is how it really is.

Well, as we have said before, meat eating leaves unused forces in man, which then start to work in such a way that bad substances are produced. Obviously they can be got rid of. But it is sometimes quite a complicated affair. Now some things said bluntly can sound rather strange. One gets to know people who work just as they choose throughout the winter and also eat as much as they like with such a degree of enjoyment that they have daily a slight indigestion, which they keep in check with the necessary drop of spirits, etc. But already by April or May they are ready for Carlsbad or some other spa. By that time they have collected so much rubbish in their bodies that they need a good mucking out. So they go to Carlsbad. You know how Carlsbad water works. It produces quite a nice little diarrhoea. So they have a good clear out and when they go back they can start again. But as a rule, all that happens is that they have to return to Carlsbad the following year. And if they are once prevented from going to a spa they readily get diabetes or something like it.

In polite society it sounds quite good if one says one is going to Carlsbad. But what it really amounts to is employing someone to come with a rubbish bin to clear out the body and put it in order again. That is what the sips of Carlsbad water do together with the effects of the baths. They act as a thorough mucking out. Then things can go on again for a time.

This however is no way to improve the general health. According to the way people eat nowadays, those that cannot go to Carlsbad get the same sort of food as those that can. It is just what is available on the market. Those who do not go to Carlsbad also have to eat. Those who have not the money to go to Carlsbad do not get cleared out. What can a person do — he cannot get anything different to eat. Medical practice will have to begin to guide social life on to the right tracks.

Well, one could go on speaking about these things for a long time. If I have forgotten anything today I will speak about it another time.

As regards absinth I will just add that it acts in a somewhat similar way to the alcohol in wine, beer etc. The difference being that alcohol wrecks the bodily substance — sleep heals this to a certain extent — but with absinth sleep is also ruined. With absinth man suffers a hangover during sleep and this prevents a proper sleep. One needs sleep when one drinks alcohol, this is what is meant by the expression 'sleeping it off'. Sleep has a beneficent effect after drinking alcohol. It counteracts it. Absinth is worse than other alcohol because this does not happen and even sleep is ruined.

You need only notice how during sleep our hair grows quicker. People who shave know that if they have slept much longer than usual they have to shave sooner than otherwise. Haven't you noticed this? (*Yes*) When the soul is not active in the body the hair grows very quickly. Sleep is there to stimulate the growth forces in the physical body. But absinth works even into the sleep and with the absinth drinker this counteraction in sleep does not take place, so that even during sleep the red corpuscles of the woman who drinks absinth are destroyed and the white corpuscles of the man.

But there is more. The monthly periods of the woman who drinks absinth are very much affected and irregularities occur in the drinker, but even more in her offspring. The result is that the discharge that should occur every four weeks is no longer regular.

So the essential thing about absinth is that it has very much the same effect as the alcohol in wine, beer and spirits, but it also ruins sleep.

7

ABSINTH. HONEY

Extract from a
Lecture to the Workmen   Dornach, 3rd February 1922

I have told you that the female element is more connected with the influences from the surrounding world while the male element shuts itself off from these influences. If men are addicted to absinth it wrecks those organs which should ensure that the offspring have strong and stable characters. So if the vice of absinth drinking spreads among men we shall get weakly offspring, weakly future generations. If in addition, women take to absinth, it will happen that the offspring will be very prone to illness. If we see women who drink absinth and they have children it will be found that these children will be very liable to all sorts of illnesses....

We can study what honey does when we eat it. Absinth unites with the fluid in man in such a way that it drives out the air and with it the soul element, and that gives a feeling of pleasure. Honey gives pleasure only on the tongue. The moment honey is eaten it assists the proper connection between the airy and fluid elements in man. Nothing is better for man than to add a little honey, but in the right measure, to his food. The bees, in a wonderful way, help man to learn how his soul should work on his organs. Through their honey, the bees give back to man what he needs for the work of his soul in the body. When he drinks absinth he wants to relish and enjoy his soul. When he adds honey to his food he wants to prepare his soul so that it works and breathes properly in the body. Bee-keeping, therefore, advances civilisation because it makes man strong. Drinking absinth, however, would drive mankind gradually to the point of extinction.

51

If one thinks how greatly the bees are influenced from the starry worlds, one sees that bees are the means of ensuring that man receives what is right for him. All that lives, works together in the right way if it is combined in the right way. When one sees a hive of bees, one should say to oneself with awe and reverence: By way of the beehive the whole universe flows into man and makes us good, capable people, but if we drink absinth it turns us into the opposite. Thus knowledge of man becomes knowledge of the universe.

8

BEETROOT

Extract from a
Lecture to the Workmen   Dornach, 5th May 1923

You can see it is like this: If one eats the root of a plant, it is, like any poisonous root, under the influence of the moon. The moon has an influence on the growth of plant roots. For this reason certain roots are very necessary for certain human constitutions.

You know that there can be a very troublesome population of the intestines — worms. For people who are prone to worms it is good to eat beetroot. Beetroot cannot enter the intestines without upsetting the worms! They become paralysed and are passed out with the faeces. So we can see that roots have an influence on this lower animal life — the worms.

Beetroot does not poison us but it poisons the worms, and you will again find that the strongest effect of the beetroot against worms is at full moon. These things must be taken into account.

If we study the plant root we find that it gives us something which works very strongly on the metabolic and limb system. One could help people with certain diseases by putting them on a root diet, so that the roots would be eaten during the time of the full moon and left off during the new moon.

Everything that one can observe regarding plants has significance for man, for his reproduction and growth. Children who do not grow can be brought on a little by giving them roots. This must be done when they are still very young, between birth and the seventh year. The forces of the moon have a great influence on the reproduction and growth of everything in the plant world, the animal world and the human kingdom.

9

POTATOES, BEETROOT, RADISHES, NUTRITION

Extract from a
Lecture to the Workmen   Dornach, 18th July 1923

You have probably heard that the potato was not introduced into Europe until a certain time. The peoples of Europe have not always been potato eaters. . . .

Let us now look at the potato. What we eat is not really the root of the potato. The roots are these small things (a drawing was made on the blackboard). If this is the potato these little rootlets are attached to it. They are removed with the peel. The potato itself is a swollen stem. An ordinary plant has a root from which the stem grows. When, however, the stem swells as it does in the potato, we have a tuber, but it is really a swollen stem. So in the potato we are not dealing with a root but with a swollen stem. Bear this in mind particularly. When one eats a potato, one eats a swollen stem. One takes one's food principally from a swollen stem. The question is: What does it mean for man that when the potato came to Europe he learnt to eat predominantly a swollen stem?

If you look at a whole plant it consists of root, stem, leaves and flower (drawing). It is interesting with the plant — the root down there comes to resemble the soil, it contains many salts, and the flower up there is of similar nature to the warm air. It is as if the warmth of the sun continually simmers in the flower. Thus the flower contains oils and fats — especially oils. So when we look at a plant we have the salts deposited down below. The root is rich in salts, the flower rich in oils.

The result is that when we eat the root we introduce

much salt into our intestines. These salts find their way to the brain and stimulate it. Salts stimulate the brain. If some-one has headaches, not migraine, but headaches that fill the whole head, it is quite good for him to eat roots. You can notice that there is a certain salty sharpness in many roots. You can tell this from the taste. When, however, you eat the flower, this part of the plant is already semi-cooked. Up there are the oils; they are something which mainly lubricate the stomach and intestines. They work on the abdomen. Doctors have to take this into account when prescribing herbal teas. No one will ever be able to influence the head if he brews a tea from flowers. On the other hand if he boils roots for the patient to drink it will have a strong effect on the head. So you see that while, in man, one goes upward from the abdomen to the head, in the plant one has to go in the opposite direction — from the flower to the root. The root of the plant is related to the head. When we consider this, it will shed light on the significance of the potato. For the potato has tubers; they are something that has not quite become root. So when one eats a lot of potatoes, one is eating mainly plants which have not quite become roots. If one restricts oneself to the consumption of potatoes and eats too many, one does not support the head sufficiently. Everything remains below in the digestive tract. So by eating potatoes, people in Europe have neglected their head, their brain. One only sees this connection when one concerns oneself with spiritual science. Then one recognises that since potato eating in Europe has increased more and more and taken the upper hand, people's heads have become less capable.

The potato stimulates mainly the tongue and the gullet. If we follow the potato plant downwards we do not quite reach the root. So it is with man. If we do not get as far as the head and remain with the tongue and gullet, they will be specially stimulated by the potato, and this is why people find the potato so palatable as an accompaniment to other food. It stimulates what is below the head and leaves the head unmolested.

If one eats beetroot, one becomes filled with a desire to think. This is quite unconscious. If one eats potatoes, one only desires to eat again soon. The potato soon makes one hungry again because it does not quite reach the head. The beetroot satisfies so quickly because — and this is important — it goes right to the head and the head is the most important. It fills the head with activity when it goes right into it. This is of course extremely disagreeable for people, that they should *think*, and therefore they love the potato sometimes better than the beetroot, because the potato does not encourage them to think. Then one becomes lazy. One is not stimulated to think and one becomes lazy about thinking. The beetroot, on the other hand, activates thinking because it is a true root. It so stimulates thinking that one really wants to think and if one does not want to think, then one does not like beetroot.

If one needs to stimulate one's thinking then one should use especially the salty stimulant of the radish for instance. If someone is not very active in the head it is good for him to add some radish to his food which will activate his thoughts a little. So you see the strange fact emerges: One can say radishes stimulate thinking. And one does not even need to be very active oneself, the thoughts simply come when one eats radishes — such strong thoughts that they even generate powerful dreams. People who eat lots of potatoes do not get strong thoughts, but they get heavy dreams. If somebody has to eat potatoes all the time, he will be actually a bit tired all the time, and will always be wanting to sleep and dream. Therefore the food that man actually receives has an important bearing on the history of civilisation.

You could say: Yes, but do we not live entirely from the substances we eat? Even this is not the truth. I have often told you that man has a new body every seven years. It

57

renews itself continually. The substances we had in our body eight or ten years ago are no longer there. They are gone. We have cut them off with our nails and hair and sweated them out in perspiration. They all disappear, some quickly, some slowly, but they all go.

Now how does one imagine these functions? One pictures it thus — I will draw it diagramatically. Here is a man. He constantly loses substances and takes in new ones. So one thinks: substances go in through the mouth and pass out through the anus and in the urine and man is just like a tube. He takes in substances by eating and keeps them for a time and then casts them out. That is just about how one thinks man is made!

But in reality nothing of earthly substance goes into man, nothing at all. It is a mere delusion. It is like this: If we eat for instance a potato this has nothing to do with the taking in anything of the potato, but the potato is just something which stimulates the jaws and gullet and so on. There the potato is active. And now there arises in us the strength to get rid of the potato again, and while we are driving it out, there comes to us from the ether — not from the solid substance — that which builds us up in the course of seven years. We do not build our body from earthly substances. What we eat we take in order to receive the necessary stimulation. In reality we build our body from what is above. So that all that people believe about foodstuffs going in one way and coming out the other, leaving something inside in the meantime, does not apply; it is only a stimulus. A counter force comes from the ether and we build our entire body from the ether. No part of us is built up from earthly substance. You see if we push something and get a counter-push, we must not confuse the second push with the original push. You must not confuse the fact that we need food in order not to become lazy in restoring our body, with the fact that the food is actually taken into the body.

Of course there can be irregularities. If we eat too much,

then food does indeed remain in us too long. Then we collect in us unwarranted substances, become corpulent, fat and so on. If we eat too little, we do not get enough stimulus and do not take up sufficient of what we need from the spiritual world — from the etheric world.

But this is something so important — that we do not build up our bodies from the earth and its substances, but from what is outside the earth. If it is true that within seven years the whole body is renewed, then the heart too will be renewed. The heart which you had 8 years ago you have no longer. It has been renewed, not by earthly substance but by what lives in the light round the earth. Your heart is compressed light. You have really compressed your heart out of the sunlight. And the food you took in was only the stimulus to compress the sunlight. All your organs are built up from what lives in the light-filled surroundings, and the fact that we eat and take in food has only significance as stimulus.

You see, the only thing that food gives us is something we have within us like a kind of inner chair. We feel ourselves, and in this way we become conscious of our ego in normal life because we have physical matter, physical substance in us. We feel ourselves in the same way as we do when we sit down on a chair. You feel the chair on which you sit pressing on you. And so you feel your body which continually presses on what you have made out of that which you have received from the world-all. When you are asleep you do not feel it because you are outside your self. You feel your body, it is a sort of couch that has been made for you, in some cases harder, if you are bony, in some cases softer. It is a kind of couch on which man lies down, and one feels the difference between a soft feather bed and a wooden bench! Likewise man feels the difference between what is hard in him and what is soft. But this is not the real man, the real man is what is within him.

PROTEIN, FATS, CARBOHYDRATES AND SALTS. POTATOES AND MATERIALISM. HYDROCEPHALUS.

Extract from a
Lecture to the Workmen   Dornach, 22nd September 1923

A question was asked about nutrition and whether the effects of eating potatoes in countries outside Europe is different.
Rudolf Steiner: Let us once again consider the question of the connection of nutrition with the spiritual world. As you know it was not until the modern age that the potato was introduced. I have told you that in earlier times people in Europe did not eat potatoes but that they lived on completely different food. The question cannot be resolved without considering the relation of the spiritual world to nutrition.

You will remember that I once spoke to you of four substances upon which man's life essentially depends. Firstly there is protein, which is really contained in all foods. It is found in its most characteristic form as albumen in the hen's egg, but it is present in all foods. Protein then is the first.

Then there are the fats. Fats are not only eaten directly as animal fats, they are contained in everything. Certain other products are transformed into fatty foodstuffs, for instance milk into cheese etc.

The third food is what we call carbohydrates. We get them from the plant kingdom. They are of course present in other foodstuffs too, but essentially in wheat, rye, lentils, beans and potatoes — especially in potatoes.

Finally there are the salts. Salts are usually considered to be mere accessories, but they play a particularly important part in man's life. The most common form, of course, is cooking salt, but all foodstuffs contain salts. It may therefore be said that in order that man may live, his food must contain protein, fats, carbohydrates and salts.

I will now speak of what these different substances, which we get in different forms in our mixed diet, do for man. Let us begin with the salts.

Even when salts are consumed in tiny quantities, they not only add flavour but are an extremely important food. We take salt with our food not only for the pleasant stimulating taste but really in order that we may be able to *think*. The salts in food must find their way up to the brain if we are to be capable of thinking. The salts are mainly connected with our thinking. If a person is so ill that all the salt in his food is deposited in the stomach or intestines and not carried by the blood into the brain, he becomes feeble-minded and dull-witted. This is an important point.

We must of course be quite clear that spirit exists, but if spirit is to be active on earth, it must work in the substances of the earth. In spiritual science, therefore, we must be able to perceive how spirit works in substance. Otherwise it would be like saying — machines are something material; we however are spiritual people, we do not want anything material, we do not want to buy iron or steel, we want to create machines out of spirit — this of course is rubbish! First one needs the substance and the creative spirit in nature needs substance everywhere. And if spirit is prevented from using substance — if the salt is deposited in the stomach and intestines instead of reaching the brain by way of the blood — then a man becomes dull-witted.

However, things are not as simple as this. Man cannot use salt as he finds it in nature. If you were to make a tiny perforation into the brain and let salt trickle in, it would be quite useless. The salt must pass into the stomach and intestines and be brought into an ever finer and finer state of solution — even on the tongue it begins to dissolve. As a result of what the human organism does with the salt, it is already in a spiritualised condition when it reaches the brain.

It is not as simple as taking salt directly into the brain. But if one is unable to have the effects of salt in the brain, one becomes feeble-minded and dull.

Now let us look at carbohydrates. They are found in peas, beans, wheat, rye and potatoes — above all in potatoes. With these we consume carbohydrates. They are largely responsible for the fact that, as man, we have the human form. If we consumed no carbohydrates we would have all kinds of malformations of the human form. For instance, it could be that the nose or ears were not properly formed. We would not have our human shape. Carbohydrates outline the shape of our body. They work in all directions outlining the human form everywhere. If man, through his constitution, is unable to direct the carbohydrates to his brain, if they are deposited in the intestines and stomach instead, then he fades away. One sees how he collapses, becomes weak, and how, to a certain extent, he can no longer maintain his form. So it is the carbohydrates which contribute to providing us with the proper human form.

So you see, for everything the appropriate foods must be taken. Salts work on the frontal part of the brain; carbo-hydrates, further back, on this layer (a drawing is made). People who cannot digest enough carbohydrates, so that they do not find their way to this layer of the brain — such people would soon become hoarse, they could no longer speak with a clear voice. So if you meet someone who has suddenly become hoarse, you can assume that there is something the matter with his digestion. He cannot digest carbohydrates in the right way. They do not go to the proper place in the brain. This impairs his breathing and his speech. So we can say: Salts influence mainly thinking, carbohydrates influence speech and everything connected with it. So we must have carbohydrates. Well now, the carbohydrates shape our form, but it is actually their aim only to give us a form. They do not fill us out. We must be filled out, and this the fats do. Whereas the carbohydrates shape our form, draw the design in the air, as it were, the fats introduce the material. Fats are responsible for depositing material substances in us in the right way, but there is something rather special about it.

I have told you before that man has an ego, an astral body, an etheric body and a physical body. Obviously fat is deposited in the physical body. In order to deposit fat so that it remains living — for we must have living fat in us — for this most important function we have the etheric body. But the astral body is the important thing for the life of feeling.

Now when somebody is awake his astral body is within him; when he is asleep the astral body is outside. When he is awake and the astral body works in the etheric body, the fat is being constantly worked upon. Fats are used to grease the body. When man is asleep and his astral body is outside, the fats are not worked upon, instead they are deposited. In the waking state fat is used to lubricate: during sleep it is deposited. We need both — deposited fats and fats which grease the body.

When somebody sleeps continually (in earlier times it happened more often, now it is rarer — a gentleman of leisure for instance doesn't do a thing) the fats are also deposited by day, in the so-called waking state which really is sleeping. Then he gets a fat paunch. Everywhere fat is deposited. For fat to be deposited in the right way, it is necessary for it to be used up in a living process, because it is constantly produced. If somebody eats as much as he uses up, that is exactly right. If somebody always eats and uses nothing, he gets pot-bellied.

What I have told you, farmers know quite well as a matter of instinct, for they make use of it for fattening pigs. When they produce fat pigs, they must see to it that these animals do not use their fat for lubrication, but that everything they eat is deposited. So their life is arranged accordingly.

It can be that someone is unable to deposit fat normally. In this case he is ill. Gentlemen of leisure are quite healthy

in this respect! They deposit fat. In the same way as carbohydrates are sometimes not deposited in the right way
and a person becomes hoarse, so it can happen that the
fats are not deposited properly but pass out with the faeces,
and then a person has not got enough fat and cannot use
it properly for lubricating. Or if we have not enough to
eat and have to go hungry, we cannot do enough greasing.
Fat is really the substance we use to fill out our bodies.
What happens to a person who either suffers from starvation
or is unable to deposit fat in his body? Such a person who
has no substance for his body, becomes more and more
spiritual. But man cannot stand becoming spiritual in this
way. The spirit burns up. He does not only become dry
and shrivelled, but gases are developed and lead to delusions
etc. and a condition develops known as starvation madness.
There is always a destruction of the spirit when a person
is ill.

So if somebody does not get enough fat, he will waste
away.

Now protein — this has to be there from the outset.
Protein is there in the egg before a being, human or animal,
develops. So we may say, protein is the substance which
builds and develops the human being. It is the primary
basis of everything. Everything in the body has to develop
from protein. You can understand this, can't you? Protein
has to be there from the beginning in order that man can
come about. The mother forms protein in the womb in
the shape of a little lump. The ovum is then fertilised and
through this the protein acquires the ability to receive
the formative forces that build man. But of course man
needs protein continually. Therefore his food has to contain
protein. If he does not get enough protein or cannot digest
it properly, then he does not only waste away because
of the lack of it — which would gradually kill him — but
if, at any moment of his life, he had no real protein at
all, he would die at once. Just as protein is necessary for

64

man to come into being, so it is absolutely necessary for his life. He who cannot digest any protein at all will die.

Let us consider the individual foodstuffs. If we look at salts, our attention will be directed mainly to the frontal part of the head. This is where salts are deposited. A little further back the carbohydrates are deposited, and they are responsible for the fact that we bear the human form. The fats are deposited even further back and from there fill out the body, for they do not go into the body directly but via the blood into the head where they are prepared and sorted out for the body. Everything goes through the head, protein included.

But there are differences regarding carbohydrates. If one takes lentils, beans, peas, rye and wheat, one can say the carbohydrates are taken from fruit. So what the earth gives you in wheat is its fruit. Lentils are also fruit. Fruits have the peculiarity that they are digested in the stomach and intestines and only send their forces up to the head. So when you eat wheat, lentils and beans, they are digested in the intestines, as you will know from the characteristic discomforts which can arise when you eat lentils or beans. The main characteristic of fruits is that they are thoroughly digested in the intestines.

But we cannot eat the fruit of the potato. If we were to eat its fruit we would take in a dangerous poison. The potato does not allow us to consume it in the same way as we do lentils, beans, peas etc. or the fruits of the field — rye and wheat. What part of the potato do we eat? The part that is below, the tuber, and tubers, roots and so on are those parts of the plant which are least digested in the intestines. Fruits are digested in the intestines. We cannot eat the fruit of the potato and the tuber is not a true root. Now we eat a potato and it goes into the stomach and the intestines. It cannot be digested there but goes up with the blood undigested. So when it arrives at the appropriate layer of the brain, it is not in the fine condition of rye or wheat which can straight away be sent into the rest of the body; it has to be worked up and digested there in the brain. So if we eat proper rye or wheat bread which we digest thoroughly in our stomach and intestines, we do not have to burden our head with digesting it. It can distribute it throughout the body straight away. Whereas, if we eat potato bread or potatoes in general, the head has to serve as a digestive organ. But if it has to do this it can no longer think, for it needs to be free to think. For this the abdomen would have to take over the work. So if man eats too many potatoes — which has happened more and more since the potato was introduced into Europe and became important — the head becomes less and less capable of thinking and man loses more and more the capacity to think with the middle of the brain; he thinks only with the frontal part. This frontal part, which depends on the salts, causes us to become more and more materialistically intellectual. Real spiritual thoughts cannot be thought by the frontal part of the brain. It makes us into a true intellectual. It is a fact that inner thinking in Europe regressed from the moment that the potato took hold.

We must remember that man is not formed by the forces of the earth alone. I have told you often that man is derived from the whole surroundings — he is a creation of the sun, moon and stars. When he eats potatoes, he uses the middle part of his brain only to digest them. He isolates himself from the surrounding world. He does not recognise it any more. He thinks it is just so much empty talk — all that is said about the universe — that there is spirituality coming down from it. So to a great extent one has to blame the excessive consumption of potatoes for the materialism of our times.

Of course, people of slender means are dependent on the potato because it is cheap, and those people who can afford to do so can buy in addition things that work on the frontal part of the brain. They can use seasoning and spices on their food. Spices work on the frontal part of the brain in the same way as salts. The result is they become intellectuals and can tell the other people what they like, because these others cannot use their heads any more for thinking. So the potato has a particular link with the spirit. It has made the spirit materialistic.

Let us look at the connections of foodstuffs with the different members of man's being. The physical body owes its origin to protein. Protein is connected with physical birth and death. The main realm of the etheric body is the fats. Carbohydrates are the principle domain of the astral body and the salts that of the ego. The capacity to feel is in the astral body. (When I hit my hand and feel it, I do not feel it with my physical body, otherwise everything of a physical nature would have the capacity to feel.) I push back the flesh, the muscle, and in this way the muscle is pushed out of the astral body and the feeling is in the astral body. All feeling is in the astral body. The astral body must be allowed to work properly. I told you that if the astral body sleeps by day as well as by night, it cannot work properly and the fat is deposited as a paunch, or if a person only works intellectually with his head and becomes an intellectual, the fat is also deposited. But the astral body which, among other things, works in the faculty of speech, needs carbohydrates not only in the head but in the whole body. The astral body moves the legs and it moves the hands. It needs carbohydrates in the whole body. If I give it rye or wheat as carbohydrates, the forces go into the whole body. If I give it only potatoes, the forces remain in the head and the person becomes emaciated, weak and his astral body cannot work properly. What is spiritual in man becomes more and more weak and sleepy if he is not able to get carbohydrates which penetrate his whole body. With an exclusive diet of potatoes, this is not possible because it makes so much work for the head that there is nothing left for the body.

What does science do? It analyses protein to see how much carbon, oxygen, nitrogen, hydrogen, sulphur, etc. are in it.

It finds there is so much per cent of carbon and so much per cent of hydrogen in protein. Fat contains a different percentage and carbohydrates are again different. But science is completely ignorant of the fact that these substances themselves have their own significance. Science only knows the percentages of the constituents. But this does not help one to get anywhere. The constituents of the potato are present in it in quite a different way from what they are in rye and wheat, and one must know that if one eats a flower or a fruit it will be digested in the intestines, while if one eats a root it will be worked upon in the head. The same thing applies when they are used medicinally. If one can understand them according to a true medical science, one knows that a tea or infusion of flowers, seeds or fruit works predominantly in the intestines. If one makes a decoction of the root, it has a healing influence on the head. If we eat roots they influence the head and what is important to know is that this influence on the head is material.

But let us go further. If somebody is not only so emaciated by a potato diet that he cannot use his hands and feet but that even the organs of reproduction are affected, then things are even worse. Let us assume that the potato diet goes so far that the female reproductive organs are affected. Man does not originate only from his ancestors but his soul/spiritual part comes from the spiritual world and unites with what comes from his ancestors. Now let us see how this happens.

Man develops from the female ovum. The male sperm penetrates it. Then all sorts of star-like shapes develop in it. Cells divide and they gradually build up the human body. But no human body can be formed if the soul/spirit part which comes from the spiritual world does not unite with what is happening.

If the mother or father have lived on an excessive potato diet, an embryo is formed which is predestined to have a head which must work too much. If you look at an embryo of somebody who is properly fed with rye bread, etc. where father and mother have proper food, then it looks like this: (drawing). But if you have an embryo whose parents have eaten excessive quantities of potatoes, the following occurs. Of course, in an embryo, one has mainly the round sphere of the head, the rest is hardly developed. Now the soul/spirit has to enter the head and when it enters the head it has to work with the head. While still in the womb the soul/spirit of man works predominantly on the head.

When the soul/spirit finds in the head what comes from the rye and wheat that the mother has eaten, it can work very well. For you see rye and wheat come from flowers which have pushed up out of the earth and therefore the spirit can meet the plant. There is a relationship. So when the soul/spirit finds in the womb what comes from fruits it can work easily. If, however, the spirit encounters in the womb the head of an embryo formed predominantly from a diet of potatoes. . . . Well as you know, the potato goes down into the earth, it is even covered with soil, one has to dig it up out of the soil, it grows in darkness and has no relationship to the spiritual. Man descends from the spiritual world and finds a head that is formed out of darkness. The spirit cannot reach it, and the result is that the embryo looks like this: (drawing). This is somewhat caricatured. A huge hydrocephalus is born. When the spirit cannot reach it, the physical grows and the hydrocephalus is formed. When the spirit *can* reach it, it keeps the water in check, it works on the physical matter and the head is properly formed. The huge heads which one sometimes sees in embryos are the result of faulty nutrition, mainly due to the potato. So you see, it is not only man himself who is debilitated but he is born with the soul and spirit not properly within his physical body.

Man consists, as we know, of physical body, etheric body, astral body and ego but they are not the same at different ages. The etheric body, astral body and the ego of the child have to submerge themselves well into the physical body. When the etheric body is completely in the physical body, then the second teeth appear. When the astral body is fully in the physical body the age of puberty is reached. When however, through a potato diet, the soul/spirit cannot take hold properly of the physical body within the womb, there is a disturbance of the processes which should take place in the fourteenth or fifteenth year. The person goes through life as though he did not possess his body — as though it were only hanging on him. So under the excessive influence of potatoes, people are born not strong enough to go through life.

These are extremely important matters. Social conditions depend on far more than one usually assumes. They also depend on the proper use of fields, that potatoes are not grown in larger quantities than people can eat while still keeping their strength. One must be concerned with real natural science if one is interested in social science. This is absolutely necessary. Talking about increased values and capital is no use at all. Let us assume that communism were to wipe out all capital, and administer everything itself — if it has only learnt from the bourgeoisie a science which does not know how to use fields properly and does not know that it is far worse to fill the stomach with potatoes than with rye and wheat, nothing will help. This is what one has to keep in mind.

HONEY AND MILK

Extracts from: 'Nine Lectures on Bees'
Lectures to the Workmen   Dornach, 26th February to
22nd December 1923

11 HONEY

From Lecture 2 (26th November 1923)

.... As we grow older, honey has an extremely beneficial effect on us. With children it is milk that has a similar effect. Honey helps the building of our bodies and is therefore strongly recommended for people who are growing old. It is an extremely wholesome food; only one must not eat too much of it. If one eats too much of it, using it not merely as an addition to one's food, the formative forces can become too strongly active. The form becomes too hard and brittle and one may develop all kinds of illnesses. A healthy person feels just how much he can eat. Honey is particularly good for older people because it gives the body the right firmness.

For children suffering from rickets one should make a rule of giving them just the right quantity of honey when they are nine to ten months old, and continue this till the age of three or four years. Rickets would then not be as serious as it is, for this illness consists in the body being too soft and collapsing. Of course, in the very first weeks of their lives children ought only to be given milk; honey at that age would have no effect. Honey contains the forces that give man's body firmness. These things should be understood. ...

12 MILK

From Lecture 5 (5th December 1923)

.... If one has a wide knowledge of people one can say: A

man — there are such men — is fairly sprightly and strong at the age of 65 or 66; another man is not so vigorous because he suffers too much hardening (calcium deposit) of the arteries, etc. To observe this, and connect it with what occurred in his childhood, is extremely interesting.

For example, one can give a child milk that comes from cows which have eaten too much fodder grown on a calcarious soil. In this way already the child takes in something of this calcarious soil. This may not be apparent at once. A doctor of the modern school may show you a child brought up on milk from cows kept on calcarious soil and another child brought up on its mother's milk and he will say: 'It makes no difference at all.' But the child brought up on its mother's milk is still sprightly at the age of 65 or 66 and the child brought up on cows' milk has arterial sclerosis at the same age. This is so because man is *a whole,* and what works in one period of time still continues to be active at a much later period. Something can be quite healthy at one time, but it works on.

13 HONEY
From Lecture 6 (10th December 1923)
.... Honey should really play a far greater role in human nutrition than it does today, if one would really grasp how immensely important honey is.

If medicine could have a stronger influence on social life, I would consider it very beneficial if people about to be married would eat honey — prophylactically so to speak. They would then not have ricketty children because honey when assimilated can affect the reproductive processes and give a proper form to the body of the child. Honey eaten by the parents, but mainly by the mother, works on the structure of the bones of the child....

14

ON NUTRITION
PROTEIN, FATS, CARBOHYDRATES, OVEREATING

Lecture to the Workmen   Dornach, 23rd January 1924

I should like to add something to what I told you last time.* We spoke about poisons and their effects on people and from this we saw that if one really understands science one must rise to the supersensible, to the spiritual members of man.

Now today, to complete the picture, I would like to add to what we have been discussing about the strong effects of poisons, something about the effects of food on the more or less healthy human body.

In the main man consumes three to four types of nutritive substances. The first is *protein* which you can best learn to understand if you look at an egg. Protein is produced by plants as well as by the animal and human body. Both the human and animal body need not only the forces which they carry within themselves for the production of protein (every living body produces protein) but they also need the protein which the plants produce. The human body also takes in animal protein. With regard to protein, science has made a fool of itself not so long ago. Only twenty years ago it was taught everywhere that man needs at least 120 grams of protein per day to maintain good health. The nations' diets were so ordered that the food prescribed contained the requisite amount of protein. It was believed that 120 grams were necessary.

Today science has gone back on this completely. It is now

* The Effects of Poisons. 9th January 1924.

known that if one eats so much protein not only does it not promote one's health but it positively promotes ill-health, for the greater part of the protein decays in the intestine. So that by eating 120 grams of protein per day one has always something like rotting eggs in the intestine which putrify its content and the resultant poison finds it way into the rest of the body and not only causes arterial sclerosis in later life (most arterial sclerosis comes from eating too much protein) but also renders people extremely susceptible to all sorts of diseases. People are more resistant to infection the less unnecessary protein they eat (naturally a certain amount is necessary). Those who eat a lot of protein are more prone to infectious diseases such as diphtheria and smallpox than people who eat less protein.

It is quite remarkable that today science teaches that it is not 120 grams which are necessary but only 20 to 50 grams. This is said to be the daily ration that man really needs. So rapidly has science changed its views in only two decades! You see how much one can depend upon what is scientifically determined. If someone by chance wishes to look up this matter and he picks up an encyclopaedia which is 20 years old, he will find he needs 120 grams of protein. If he picks up a more recent edition he will read: 20-50 grams, and if he consumes more he will become ill. So you see how it is with scientific truths. One gets informed of what is right or wrong according to which edition of the encyclopaedia one happens to pick up. All this shows that in matters reaching into spiritual dimensions it is impossible to arrive at the truth in this manner. It makes us realise, when we really think about it, that one must enter the spiritual realm if one would understand what happens when a person eats protein. It is the one foodstuff which under all circumstances has to be dealt with in the intestines and the abdomen must have the power to deal with it. You know that albumen, especially when fresh, is semi-liquid. All albumen is semi-liquid. The human etheric body can find its way to every-

74

thing that is semi-liquid. It can do nothing with solid matter, only with liquids. So man must take all his food in a fluid condition.

Now you will say: But if someone takes salt or sugar or suchlike, they are solid. However they will be dissolved immediately. That is what we have saliva for. Solids which constitute physical bodies must, under no circumstances, enter the human body from the world outside. From this you can infer: You have solid substances in you, as you know — the bones are solid. But in reality the solid bones are formed out of the fluid element in the human body. Nothing solid from outside can ever get into the human body. The human body has to let everything solid arise out of the fluid element. So you can say: we have solid matter in us, and this builds up the physical body. But the physical body is formed entirely out of the fluid element and for this element there is the etheric body, this fine body which one cannot see, though it permeates the whole man. Protein too must be transformed by the etheric body, and as we said before, in the abdomen. Of course, the other spiritual members of man's being also are active in it, as I have told you already, but protein must be dealt with in the etheric body. The fluid is there for the etheric body. Now because you know that protein must be worked upon in the abdomen, you can see that protein cannot demand the most strenuous work in our body, it does not have to work up into the chest and above all not up into the head. So you see that protein cannot serve man as a food of primary importance. One can even say it is almost impossible for man to eat too little protein, for what one eats reaches the abdomen very quickly, it does not require much work. The abdomen deals with it. Even if one has a low protein diet, all the protein will be immediately transformed.

All this goes to show that it is quite possible for man to live on a diet including very little protein. Today science admits this, but years ago children in particular were overfed with protein. Today we see these children who were overfed with protein in the seventies and eighties of the last century. They go about with arterial sclerosis or have already died of it. The harmfulness of a thing does not show immediately, but only much later.

The *fats* are the second sort of nutritive substance. Fats, when eaten, also pass of course into the abdomen. But the fats pass through the intestines and work very strongly on the central part of man's body — the chest. Man absolutely needs fats for the nourishment of his heart, chest, etc.

The reason why man needs fats for his chest region is because his breathing is located there. What does this mean? It means that the carbon that we carry within us combines with oxygen. For carbon to combine with oxygen one needs heat. What the fats do while they combine with oxygen is to generate heat. So the fats contribute a great deal to what man needs in his chest organisation. Now we said that proteins, when they are not transformed by the body in the abdomen, are inclined to decay. When we have inadequately transformed protein in us we really have something like rotten eggs in our intestines. No doubt you know the smell of rotten eggs, and the thing is that if people eat too much protein this rotten egg substance is discharged into the body. They are permeated with this rotten egg substance. If you keep eggs too long they become rotten eggs and they also stink like rotten eggs. And you see that part which the body has not transformed is obviously going to stink in it; but the other part which has been transformed passes into the body in a pure state. This is the work of the etheric body. The etheric body has the task of removing the rotten stink and overcoming it. In the human body the etheric body is the fighter and conqueror of decay. Rotting is vanquished by the etheric body. After death, when man no longer has his etheric body, decomposition sets in. Here you have it quite tangibly: while man lives he does not decompose, when he no longer lives, he does. Why? Because the etheric body has left him after death. The etheric body is that part of man which prevents decay. We have in us continually the battle against decomposition, and the fighter is the etheric body.

I think that whosoever marshals all these facts must see with the greatest clarity from mere external observation that an etheric body must exist, that in fact an etheric body must be everywhere. Imagine that everywhere on the earth proteins are produced which rot. The earth would stink to high heaven if the ether were not there to drive away the putrefaction. So inside and outside the human organism is the ether which continually fights against the rotting of protein substances. This must always be borne in mind.

With regard to fats, it is so that they do not rot, they become rancid, as you all know. Even butter goes rancid. It is the peculiarity of fats that they go rancid. If you keep butter for a time, you cannot tell by looking at it if it is rancid or fresh, if you are not trained. But if you put it on the tongue and taste it, then you immediately know that this butter is rancid. It has something to do with the consciousness, with feeling. Rotting has something to do with smell, with something external, you can smell it. Rotting eggs are naturally different from the scent of roses, and you can smell it. Not so when something becomes rancid; it needs to be tasted, which is a more inward process.

This points to the fact that this has more to do with a more inward feeling than in the case of rotting eggs. All that is *feeling* in our consciousness is connected physically with our middle system — our chest — but spiritually with the astral body. And you know that within the chest the airy element is active. We breathe in air. We transform the air. Air is at home in the chest. In the other parts of the human body gasses and air should only be produced very sparingly. If too much gas is produced in the intestines, flatulence ensues, which is unhealthy. The middle system is the appropriate place for gas. And the higher supersensible member which takes hold there is the human astral body.

77

This astral body fights to prevent fats becoming rancid, just as the etheric body combats the rotting of protein substances. Man would continually have rancid eructations (belching) from his own fats, he would taste rancid to himself if his astral body did not continually fight rancidity. So we have the astral body within us to combat the rancidity of fats.

You see how wonderful this is. What is outside in the ordinary physical material world goes in quite another direction to what is inside us. Outside us in the physical world fats go rancid under all circumstances. Man, luckily does not always go rancid, only when he is internally ill, for the astral body of a man in good health ensures that he does not go rancid. He only becomes rancid when he eats so much fat that the astral body cannot cope with it, or if, for some reason, too much fat is produced. Man perceives inwardly his own rancidity. When he is very rancid, which means that the working of the astral body is very insufficient, he has always a bad taste in his mouth. This unpleasant taste reflects back on the stomach. In this roundabout way man gets gastric and intestinal illnesses from rancid fat within him.

For a person who is inwardly rancid, because he has in him too many fats that he cannot transform, arsenic is a good remedy. Arsenic [homoeopathically] combats the accumulation of fat, it strengthens the astral body. And the result is, the person can fight this rancidity. These things are extremely important. If a person shows a tendency of being unable to overcome his rotting protein with his etheric body, then usually a very effective remedy is some compound of copper. Copper is effective when abdominal intestinal illnesses are directly due to protein. But if something is noticeable about the taste in the mouth, it does not help to use copper; it must be arsenic, because his astral body must first be strengthened. So it does not suffice if one finds this or that illness in this or that part of the body; one must know the cause — rotting protein in the intestines or rancid fats which work back into the intestines and stomach via the bad taste in the mouth.

So you see within us substances behave in the opposite way to what they do outside. We have the astral body which prevents fats from becoming rancid, while in the ordinary physical material world fats simply go rancid.

A third constituent of man's food is the *carbohydrates*. They are found mainly in potatoes for instance, in lentils and beans, and of course in all cereals. This is where they are found. Many of these either contain sugar (we always include some sugar in our food) or sugar is produced directly from these carbohydrates. We take in for instance what is in the potato and transform it. The potato contains a great deal of starch and this starch is transformed first into dextrin and then into sugar. So if you eat potatoes, you are really taking sugar, since the potato starch is transformed into sugar in the human body. Now grapes for instance contain a lot of sugar. Consequently alcohol also does. What alcohol is for man — apart from the alcohol itself — has to do with its sugar content. The human organism transforms alcohol into sugar.

The first kind of foodstuff is protein, the second fats and the third starch, sugar. We have seen that protein is worked upon by the etheric body so that it does not putrefy. Fats are worked upon by the astral body so that they do not become rancid. Now — starch and sugar? The etheric body is active mainly in the abdomen, the astral body above all in the chest system. Now we come to something different. You all know — I do not say from your own personal experience, but from seeing people who are not like yourselves — the effects of alcohol, and you know that it produces special symptoms — first drunkenness, but we will not speak of this now. But you know that the next day — we have already gone into this — you have a bad head, a hangover. What does this signify in the nutrition process?

The fact that you have it in the head shows that it has

something to do with the head. And when people tell you the next day (those who are not like you) how they had been drunk the day before, they complain about their head. They have a headache, and if it is not a headache, then it feels as if their head would fall off their shoulders, and so on. What is really happening?

The main task of the head is to oppose what starch and sugar wish to do. What *do* they wish to do? You need only look at wine. When autumn comes the grapes are gathered, they are pressed and then the juice ferments. When it has ceased fermenting it is drunk as wine. By having fermented into wine, it has overcome fermentation. When the wine reaches the stomach something arises from it which goes into the food. One can say, the alcohol is re-transformed back. And now starch and sugar are the substances which want to ferment. In the human organism they have a tendency to ferment. When you drink alcohol it drives out of your head the forces that would prevent the fermentation of sugar and starch. Let us make it quite clear. Supposing on the 22nd of January you have eaten potatoes and beans and have drunk alcohol with them. All right. If you had not drunk alcohol your head would have remained sober. Potatoes and beans contain starch and sugar. The head has the forces to prevent the fermenting of starch and sugar. If you introduce alcohol, the head loses the capacity to prevent this fermentation of starch and sugar which are contained in the potatoes you have eaten. The potatoes and beans and other things such as cereals, begin to ferment inside you.

You see, instead of the fermentation in man being prevented, it takes place, and this through an inability of the head due to the alcohol, so that man is now full of the forces of fermentation. In central Germany, in Thuringia, there is a strange saying. When someone talks nonsense, they say in Thuringia: 'He is fermenting', (bubbling up). In these parts one does not usually say, if someone talks nonsense, that he is fermenting. Those of you who have been to Germany — central Germany — may have come across this saying. So in central Germany, fermentation is linked with a muddled head and nonsense. This is a very sound instinct. One knows that there is too much fermenting in a person when he talks nonsense. When someone has got a bad head from drinking alcohol, he does not talk nonsense, he becomes quiet, but the nonsense is in him and buzzes in his head. The tangible effect of alcohol is therefore that starch and sugar are no longer prevented from fermenting, while normally the head prevents it.

Just as the etheric body is mainly situated in the abdomen, the astral body in the chest, so, as no one will deny, the ego is mainly situated in the head. We also have to see it like this: the physical body has to do with the solid, the etheric body with the fluid, the astral body with the gaseous, likewise the ego with warmth. Anything to do with man's ego brings warmth into motion. This can be traced in detail in the human body. The real ego is also connected with the blood and that is why the blood produces warmth. But this ego which man experiences in his consciousness is also connected with the secretion of the glands. It is also the real ego which, from the supersensible, prevents fermentation acting through the forces of the head. Thus we can say that the etheric body combats the putrefaction of protein, the astral body combats rancidity and the ego combats the fermentation of sugar and starch.

This is also the reason why I once told you that the excessive consumption of potatoes is detrimental to the head. The excessive consumption of potatoes influences man in the following way. You see the potato does not contain much protein. This makes it a good food for man. And when he eats potatoes moderately, together with other things, they are a good food because of their low protein content. But the potato contains a great deal of starch which has to be transformed into sugar in man — first into dextrin, and

81

then into sugar. As I have said, if man eats too much potato, his head must work terribly hard — obviously, since it has to prevent fermentation. This is why people who eat excessive quantities of potatoes — and have to overwork their heads counteracting their fermentation — become weak in the head. The middle part of the brain is especially affected. The frontal part of the brain remains comparatively unaffected, as it is little concerned with the prevention of fermentation. And so it has happened that through the widespread consumption of potatoes in recent times, materialism has arisen, because it originates in the frontal part of the brain.

You see it is rather strange. People believe that materialism is the outcome of logic. In a certain sense present-day materialism is nothing more than the result of eating potatoes! Now people do not like it if they have to live entirely on potatoes, do they? but they do like materialism. So here we have a contradiction. If one wants to be a thorough materialist one should have to recommend the widespread eating of potatoes; that would be the best way of making materialism convincing, but with most people it is not successful. If the materialistic monists wanted to fight successfully, they should see to it that all other foodstuffs were replaced by potatoes. Then the monists would register a tremendous success. Though not very quickly, but in the course of a few decades, monism could gain its ends if it could influence potato eating. But the people they want to influence through potato eating would probably laugh behind their backs, and then they would not be terribly successful.

But you can learn one thing from this. Spiritual science as practised here, knows the right sort of materialism. Materialism knows nothing about anything material and spiritual science recognises this. The potato is the real producer of materialism. It is very treacherous, this potato, it is cunning and sly to excess ... for you see, man can only eat the tuber, not even the eyes — even these are harmful — and the flower is quite inedible because the potato is of the

82

nightshade family and its flowers are poisonous. But what is poison? I told you last time that, taken in quantity, poison kills but in small amounts, highly diluted, it is a remedy. Potatoes contain a lot of starchy substance. They are nearly all starch and they would not even be able to exist because the starch is terribly harmful to themselves. So instantly they suck in poison from the outside world and counteract the harmful effect. This is why I call them cunning and sly. They themselves have their poison to counteract the harm to themselves. But for man the potato poison is particularly harmful. So he does not get it. He only gets what the potato itself fights against with its poison. So one can really call the potato a sly, cunning entity. And man must be quite clear about this: if he eats too many potatoes the central part of his brain deteriorates and it is even possible that the senses may be affected by excessive consumption of potatoes.

When someone as a child or a very young person is given too many potatoes, the central part of his brain becomes weak. But this is where the most important sense organs originate. The corpus quadrigemina and the thalamus opticus etc. are located there and even poor sight can therefore be the result of the excessive consumption of potatoes. And some eye troubles in old age can be traced back to being brought up on too many potatoes. People then get poor sight and weak eyes. It is really true that in the old days Europeans suffered far less from weak eyes than nowadays. And this comes — apart from other things affecting the eyes, electric light etc. which are not so bad since they do not act from within — from the excessive consumption of potatoes, which is so bad for the eyesight and even for the sense of taste. The following can happen. Supposing someone eats too many potatoes as a child. In later life one will find that such a person does not know when he has had enough because his sense of taste is spoiled by potato eating, while a person who has not eaten too many potatoes knows by instinct when he has had enough. This instinct which is connected with the mid-brain is damaged by excessive potato consumption. This is what has become very apparent in recent times.

From all I have told you, you can see that man must be very aware of the fact that he must be strong enough to overcome first the rotting of protein, secondly the becoming rancid of fats and thirdly the fermentation of starch and sugar. One cannot be a complete total abstainer, for even if one does not drink any alcohol, one still has it because one produces it in oneself. But this alcohol remains in the abdomen. It does not go up into the head because the head must be free of alcohol, otherwise as bearer of the ego it will be unable to combat the fermentation in the body in the right way. Now you can form an idea of how man is related to nature around him. If you look at the protein which rots all around — animals decay, plants decay — so you will have to agree that there must be ether everywhere which, in time, counteracts it. If you consider the fats which are also in plants, which are in fact everywhere, you will have to agree that these fats would gradually render life impossible for living things, animal and human, if the astral body did not prevent them becoming rancid. Man really fights what is outside in nature. And when man dies the etheric and astral bodies and the ego leave the physical body. Man passes out into the spiritual world. What happens then? You know what happens. The corpse immediately decays and becomes rancid and ferments. So it is really the case that when the ego leaves, the human body starts to ferment, when the astral body departs, man becomes rancid, and when the etheric body withdraws, decay sets in. Man carries all this within him, but as long as he is alive on earth he continually combats it. Whoever would deny that man bears within him an etheric body, an astral body and an ego as real spiritual entities, should be asked: How do you explain why man does not decay? Why does he not ferment?

84

Why does he not become rancid? This would actually happen if he were only a physical body.

But what does our science do? It waits till man is dead to study him. For what it knows of man in life is precious little compared to what it knows of his anatomy when he is a corpse, when he is dead. Science always waits for the corpse. So this science cannot know anything about the real man as he lives, because it does not even consider him as such. And this is the trouble with our science. Since the 17th century all its knowledge is fundamentally derived from the corpse. But the corpse is no longer the person. So one must ask: What is it that makes the corpse (which we carry about with us when we are alive) not behave as a corpse which rots, ferments and becomes rancid? It is when one considers the living human being that one really comes to accept the spiritual, supersensible members of man's being. And then one notices that the ego is active particularly in the head, the astral body particularly in the chest and the etheric body in the abdomen. Science does not even know anything about the abdomen because it thinks that the same processes take place there as outside in nature. And this is not so.

It is interesting to look at things, not shut up in one's study but outside in the middle of life. There are, as you know, spas where it smells of rotten eggs, for instance Marienbad. There are also spas in Germany which contain sulphuretted hydrogen, which is the stuff that smells of rotten eggs. Even people who are very fastidious about taste and smell are obliged to go to these watering places. And why do they do this? Why do they sometimes spend several summer months in places where it smells as if everything were sprayed with rotten eggs? These people have eaten far too much protein and therefore go to the spa. Because they are covered with skin and the smell is kept inside the skin, they themselves do not smell, but if it were possible to smell it, one would know how they stink of

85

rotten eggs inside. Now these people smelling inwardly of rotten eggs go to the spas which smell of rotten eggs and what happens there? In one case the rotten egg smell is inside, in the other case outside. When the smell is inside the nose does not notice it, when it is outside, the nose does. Head and belly are opposites. The rotten egg smell produced in the belly is neutralised by the smell which reaches the head. And so the rotten egg smell of the spas fights the rotten egg smell inside.

It is particularly noticeable for a person who has a sense for observing such things. As a boy I had by chance to go to such a spa. Every other day I had to go to Bad M.... There it stank of rotten eggs. While outside the smell was terribly unpleasant, suddenly one started to feel particularly well inside. If one is not ill, has no rotten egg smell inside, one experienced a heightened sense of well-being. If one is not put off by the smell, one can experience this. Of course, if one stops one's nose, one does not get this complementary reaction, one does not have this spring-like effect in the abdomen which one has when one surrenders to the smell of rotten eggs. This smell is a very effective remedy even if it is produced artificially. For instance it gives the body its power to make failing muscles firm and strong again. Now people do not like such cures, but they are very useful in a certain sense; for you see when the smell of rotten eggs reaches man from outside, then there is 'spring' inside. In spring everything sprouts and shoots and man can regain his strength when it is spring in his belly.

This is what happens to people who, by their gluttony in winter, ruin their digestion. People who do *not* do this will experience an inner spring at the same time when there is spring outside. The abdomen in particular participates in nature's spring. But if one really wants to do this, one must eat as little as possible of such things as pâté de fois gras, etc. If one has eaten a lot of fois gras there is no spring in

86

the belly but it is like winter in the ground. There it is warm. Potatoes are clamped below ground. But in man everything starts to decompose when such warmth is kept in him, and then spring does not come and an artificial spring must be sought in the rotten egg smell.

Thus the ego and the etheric body stand in opposition. They must reach an equilibrium in man. You see, if only one really studies nature — if one goes to a spa which smells of rotten eggs (sulphuretted hydrogen) with open senses — the feeling of spring within makes one realise how the decomposition of protein inside man produces the opposite effect.

I wanted to add this to what I told you last time. You know I said when someone has taken certain poisons, they should be given egg beaten up in water as an antidote. But wholesome things become poisons in the body if the body cannot cope with them — if too much is taken. Protein [as white of egg] can neutralise a poison in man but it is itself a poison if it decomposes in the body when too much is taken in. So close to each other are nutrition and poisoning. You will know yourselves how food can become poison. A great many illnesses are caused by faulty nutrition i.e. no account is taken of the fact that only a certain amount of any substance can be taken if it is to be properly digested.

solids : physical body	protein: etheric body, abdomen
fluids : etheric body	fats : astral body, chest
gases : astral body	starch : ego
warmth: ego	

The etheric body combats rotting
The astral body combats rancidity
The ego combats fermentation.

ALCOHOL

Extract from a
Lecture to the Workmen   Dornach, 16th February 1924

Alcohol is such a problem because talking about it is not much use if it does not lead to giving it up. For when a person starts and drinks one or two glasses he gets into a state when explanations cease to have any effect and then he continues to drink. This is why it is so extraordinarily difficult, particularly with alcohol, to achieve much by talking. It is a sad reflection on the strength of mind of mankind when one has to resort to laws instead of explanation. There are countries — think only of the United States — where alcohol is prohibited* in order to keep mankind reasonable. When it comes to the point that mankind only remains reasonable or even useful when everything is prescribed by law, then really mankind on earth is no longer worth much.

As I have told you, man produces alcohol in his own body. That is because he needs it to preserve himself. And you can be sure that from the alcohol he produces himself he will never get drunk! There is just the right quantity needed in order to preserve foodstuffs, to preserve all that needs to be kept for some time. You can well imagine, can you not, for what purpose one needs the alcohol that one produces. You will know that if one wants to preserve a dead animal or a human limb one cannot leave it exposed to the air, one puts it in spirit — in alcohol. So alcohol preserves the form of the living when it is dead. This is a very important

* In 1922 there was prohibition. Trans.

law of nature. What happens when you leave to ordinary nature something dead that was once alive? The moment the human body is given over to the earth it disintegrates, doesn't it? It is thus with everything living. The moment the etheric body leaves the living, the living is destroyed. But not if a product such as alcohol is used. Thus alcohol has the power to keep intact those forces which hold together a living limb.

From this you can see that alcohol is not earthly. From something else too you can see that it is not really normally earthly. The human body and animal and plant bodies are destroyed by earthly forces, but by alcohol they are preserved, maintained and protected from destruction.

Now how does alcohol arise? You only need to look at the vine. Alcohol arises just where the sun shines most favourably on the vine. You know that in Northern Germany no wine is produced because it is too cold. The sun there has no longer the necessary power. Fewest people get drunk on wine from Grünberg in Silesia because it is as sour as it can be! Only where the power of the sun acts on the plants can wine be produced. Thus wine is not made from earthly but actually from extra-terrestrial forces, from what is akin to the sun, from what is beyond the earth.

How does it happen that man produces his own alcohol within himself? [This rather long discursive paragraph has been condensed.] The power of the sun is everywhere, not only where it shines directly but in other ways. Leave a chair in the hot sun for a few hours and sit on it. It is very hot. It is an ordinary lifeless body that has absorbed the sun's heat and gives it back to you. In the case of coal it is very much more complicated. Thousands and thousands of years ago coal was palm-like trees and other trees. The sun shone upon them. They perished, and even as the heat of the sun remained in the chair, so it remained in these trees and went down with them into the earth. The trees turned into coal and the sun's heat remained within. After thousands of years the coal is dug out, it is put in your stove and the heat of the sun comes back to you. You are warmed today by the heat of the sun that shone on the earth thousands of years ago. People do not often realise this. Wherever there is coal in the earth − in the coal mines − there lie very old sun forces.

You eat plants. You put them inside you. Your own organism works more quickly than the earth. Within you the life-endowed carbon from the plants is quickly transformed and you get in your own body carbonic acid. This carbonic acid within you does not turn into coal as it does in the earth but it remains carbonic acid. Now in this carbonic acid you have coal within you, and from the air and foodstuffs you have oxygen. Thus we have carbon and oxygen. But in the human body you also have hydrogen − you drink water − and this hydrogen combines with the carbon and oxygen....

Now by means of those substances which you have taken in through the sun... you move around, needing in order to live, oxygen, carbon and nitrogen, and you form alcohol in your organism. This is produced in order that we do not decay inside. The body would disintegrate like a corpse does if alcohol and alcohol-like substances were not produced. That is an obvious fact. But now we must ask: On which of our bodies does alcohol actually work? On the physical body alcohol works extremely beneficially at first, if it is drunk in moderation, for if a person produces too little alcohol himself there is a good means of preservation available in alcohol. Alcohol is not at all damaging to the physical body. If it damaged the physical body it would be a poor lookout for the vine, for the vine also has a physical body. The vine is completely intoxicated (it really is, because it has pure alcohol in it) but its physical body does not suffer in the least. Neither does the etheric body suffer from alcohol. It is only the astral body in adults that suffers from alcohol. For the child it is particularly damaging because something else happens, as I will tell you shortly. But in

90

adults alcohol works on the astral body just as arsenic does, and particularly on the ego itself. The ego lives in the circulation of the blood. So alcohol works tremendously powerfully on the blood circulation.

The reason it is so bad for children is because alcohol already has an astral body itself. The plant has only an etheric body, but alcohol, which is present in the vine, already has an astral body. It acts like that which works in the blood. This is understandable, is it not? And so it comes about that if the child drinks alcohol in its early years it actually gets an astral body which should only be fully formed in its fourteenth or fifteenth year. This [other premature] astral body is not under its control. This is why alcohol is particularly damaging for a child because under the influence of alcohol it also gets an astral body.

From this you can see that alcohol really works into the soul-spiritual part of man. There it is active. It disturbs the breathing and the blood circulation which have their origin in the soul-spiritual realm. There alcohol penetrates.

* * * * *

[A question had been asked by someone who could not take any alcohol, not even one glass of beer, because the following morning little granules formed in his eyes.]

When someone cannot take alcohol, that really means he cannot properly digest it and then it goes to the head undigested and can affect the eyes and cause mucus substance to press upwards towards the head. Just as in the drinker with 'a good head' the blood is excited, so in someone who cannot stand much alcohol the mucus is activated and it coagulates and so produces little granules. These are hardened mucus. This can happen to someone who cannot stand even one glass. In the case of the person with a good head the alcohol goes straight into the blood and these granules in the eyes do not appear, but the whole circulation of the blood is stimulated and substances are secreted which are damaging. There follows the usual stupor and the familiar hangover and the person gets into the state where he goes on drinking. Thus one can see how alcohol affects people differently.

One might say: Really one should not need to differentiate, for in all cases where a particular abnormal reaction to alcohol occurs, it should be given up. It is not good to go on drinking if one feels any kind of reaction to alcohol.

As has been said, alcohol today works on the ego and the astral body. The ego feels stimulated. A person enjoys alcohol and therefore he really feels that he gets something from it that lifts him above the earthly realm. This feeling is really very interesting for, as I told you, alcohol does not originate from the earthly but from the not-earthly. That is why a person feels himself raised above the earthly. Alcohol banishes care, does it not? Thus by means of it a person comes a little out of himself and this makes him feel extraordinarily well. To a large extent this is exactly what leads to drunk and disorderly behaviour.

16

OPIUM

Extract from a
Lecture to the Workmen   Dornach, 20th February 1924

Question: I would like to know the difference between alcohol and opium. From Dr. Usteri's article one must assume that the poppy juice draws upwards and alcohol downwards.

Rudolf Steiner: What we must ask is: When a man drinks alcohol, which part of his being is influenced? The ego. The physical tool of the ego is the blood circulation. It reveals the influence of alcohol on the ego. Man's blood circulation, on which his life depends, is particularly influenced by alcohol.

But opium works particularly strongly on the astral body in such a way that man's astral body is drawn out of his physical body. This drawing out gives him a very pleasant feeling. He has got rid of his physical body for a time and this gives him this pleasant feeling.

People say casually — you will have heard this — sleep is sweet. As regards sleep man cannot feel this sweetness because he is asleep. He cannot feel it, he can only have a foretaste of it, and because he has this anticipation people say: sleep is sweet. But when man takes this poppy juice — opium — he feels this sweetness because the connection with his body is the same as if he were asleep, but he is awake. Therefore he can enjoy this sweetness, he can feel it and it fills him with great pleasure. It is as if his whole body was saturated with sugar, with a quite special sugar, full and full of sweetness. But at the same time his astral body is freed from the physical body, and consequently he perceives all kinds of things but not distinctly. He does not have ordinary dreams but perceives the spiritual world. He goes on long journeys through the spiritual world. He likes this. He is lifted up, as you said, lifted up into the spiritual world. When he drinks alcohol, on the other hand, his physical body is completely engaged, right into the blood. His astral body is not freed. The physical body is far more engaged than it is normally. The physical body dominates. This is the difference. With opium the soul/spirit is freed. Firstly it enjoys the sweetness of the physical body and secondly it travels. It enters the spiritual world in a chaotic way and therefore travels in it. The oriental people get much of what they say about the spiritual world in a wrong way. They get it from opium, hashish and the like.

17

THE CONNECTION
BETWEEN FOOD & THE HUMAN BEING:
RAW FOODS AND VEGETARIAN DIET

Lecture to the Workmen   Dornach, 31st July 1924

A question was asked about food — beans, carrots and so on, and what influence they have on the body. Some vegetarians do not eat vegetables that hang down like beans and peas. If one passes by a cornfield, one begins to think about bread grains which probably all peoples of the earth use in some form.

Rudolf Steiner: So you wish me to speak about the connection between food and the human being. Well, first of all it is necessary to be clear about what nutrition is. Usually one imagines that nutrition consists of taking in food through the mouth and into the stomach, that it is then deposited somewhere in the body, and then one eliminates it and has to start eating again and so on. But it is not as simple as this. Things are much more complicated. If one wants to understand the connection between man and his food, one must first understand what is the nature of the essential foodstuffs that man needs.

You see, the first thing that man needs — that he absolutely must have — is protein. Protein he must have. Let us write down protein so that we have it all before us. So protein — as we find it, for instance, in eggs — is not only found in eggs, but in all foods. Man must have protein. The second thing that he needs is fat. Again, fats are found in all foods. Plants also contain fats. The third has a name with which you will not be so familiar, which however one ought to know — carbohydrates. For instance the potato consists mainly of this substance, but all other plants also contain a lot of it. Carbohydrates have the peculiarity that when eaten, they transform themselves slowly, by means of the saliva and stomach juices, into starch. Starch is something that man must have. He does not eat starch but he eats foods which contain carbohydrates. They transform themselves within him into starch and during further digestion they again transform themselves and become sugar. And man must have sugar. So with carbohydrates he gets his sugar.

But there is something else that man needs. These are the salts. He gets them partly by adding salt to his food, but also partly from the food itself, all of which contains salts.

When we look at protein we must consider the great difference which exists between animal and man on the one hand, and plants. Plants also contain protein but they do not eat protein. So where do they get it from? They get it from the soil, from the air, from the lifeless, from the mineral. They are indeed able to make protein from the lifeless. Neither animal nor man can do this. Man cannot make protein from the lifeless, if he could he would only be a plant. He must take in protein which is already prepared by plants or animals. In fact man needs plants in order to live on the earth. And the interesting thing is that plants could not exist if man was not there. But isn't it interesting, gentlemen, if you really look at it, that the two most important things for life are the green sap in the plant leaf and, on the other hand, the blood. This green stuff in the plant is called chlorophyll. The green leaf contains chlorophyll. And then the blood is important. Here there is something remarkable. When you consider man, firstly he breathes. Breathing is also nourishment. Man takes up oxygen from the air. He breathes in oxygen. But everywhere in his body, carbon is deposited. If you find yourself underground in a coal mine, there you will come upon the black coal. If you sharpen a pencil you come upon graphite. Coal and graphite are carbon. Apart from other substances, you consist of carbon throughout your whole body. This is made in the human body. Now you can say: well, man is rather like a black golliwog with all this carbon. But you can also say something different. You see the most precious stone in the world, the diamond, is also made of carbon, but in a different form. So if you prefer it, you can say as regards your carbon, you consist entirely of diamonds. The dark carbon, the graphite of the pencil, and the diamond are the same substance. If the coal that comes from the dark earth could by some means be made transparent, then it would be a diamond. We have everywhere these diamonds deposited within us. So we are a real coal mine. When however the oxygen in the blood meets the carbon, then carbonic acid (carbon dioxide) is formed. You are quite familiar with carbonic acid. You need only take mineral water — there are bubbles — these are carbonic acid, which is a gas. So now you can see the whole thing. Man breathes in oxygen with the air, the oxygen spreads throughout the blood. The blood takes up carbon and carbonic acid is exhaled. You breathe in oxygen, you breathe out carbonic acid.

Through the processes which I have described, everything during the evolution of the earth would long ago have been poisoned through carbonic acid by man and animal. For all this has been going on for a long time. As you see, man and animal would have ceased to exist long ago were it not for the plants which have a completely different nature. Plants do not suck in oxygen, but the carbonic acid which is exhaled by man and animal. So the plant craves for carbonic acid just as man craves for oxygen.

You now have this plant — root, stem, leaves and flower. Everywhere it sucks in carbonic acid — it goes in. Now the carbon in the carbonic acid is deposited in the plant and the oxygen is expelled. It is there again for man and animal. Man gives off carbonic acid and kills everything. The plant keeps the carbon and lets the oxygen go and with it gives life to everything. The plant could do nothing with the carbonic acid if it had not chlorophyll. This green chlorophyll is a magician. It keeps the carbon in the plant and releases the oxygen. The blood combines the oxygen with carbon. The chlorophyll takes the carbon out of the carbonic acid and sets the oxygen free.

Think what a perfect arrangement this is in nature, that plants, man and animals complement each other in this way! They are entirely complementary.

But one must add that man does not only need the oxygen which the plant gives him but he needs the whole plant. With the exception of poisonous plants and such plants that contain minimal nutrients, man needs all plants. He takes them in, not through respiration, but as food. And here again is another remarkable connection. The plant consists of the root (the annual plant, we will not now consider trees,) leaves, flower and fruit. Let us look at the root. The root is in the soil and contains many salts because salts are in the soil. And the root clings with its fine rootlets to the soil and constantly draws salts from it. So the root is that part of the plant which is particularly connected with the mineral kingdom of the earth, with the salts.

Now you see, the human head is related to the whole earth, not the feet, but the head is related to the earth. When man begins to become earthly man in the mother's womb, he is at first almost only head. He begins with the head. The head is built on the pattern of the Universal All, but also of the Earth. And the head particularly needs salts. From the head proceed the forces which also, for instance, cause the bones to set in the body. Everything that makes man solid proceeds from the head formation. When the head itself is still soft, as it is in the womb, it cannot form proper bones. As the head itself becomes harder and harder it transfers its form to the body, so that man and animal can form the solid parts, namely the bones. So you see that one needs the root that is related to the earth and contains salts (one needs salts to form bones, bones consist of calcium carbonate and calcium phosphate — these are salts), one needs the root to provide for the human head.

If one notices for instance that a child becomes weak in the head — how does one notice this? Sometimes one can recognise certain symptoms. If a child becomes weak in the head it will easily develop worms in the intestines. Worms live in the intestines when the head forces are too weak, because the head does not work strongly enough into the rest of the body. Worms can find no abode in man if the head forces work strongly enough down into the intestines.

This is one of the best examples of how wonderfully everything is arranged in the human body. Everything hangs together. So if one has a child with worms one should conclude that it is weak in the head. One can also say — especially those who would be educationalists should know such things — that if one finds people who, later in life, are weak in the head, they will have had worms in childhood. What should one do when one notices this? The simplest thing is to take carrots and feed the children on these for a time, together with other things. Of course one must not continue to feed them entirely on carrots, but only for a time. Carrots are the most truly *root* of all vegetables. They contain many salts. Because they have the forces of the earth, they have the property, when they are taken into the stomach, of working right into the head by way of the blood. Only substances rich in salts are able to reach the head. Root substances rich in salts strengthen man through the head. This is extremely important. And it is particularly the carrot that makes the uppermost part of the head strong. So this is what one needs for man to become inwardly strong and firm, and not soft and delicate.

If you look at a carrot you will say: I can see something specific about this plant, its growth concentrates towards the root. The carrot is almost all root. The root holds one's interest if one looks at this plant. The rest of the plant only

99

sits on top of it and is of no significance. So the carrot is especially suitable food to provide for the human head. If you have a sort of empty feeling in the head and cannot think very well, it would be good to add carrots to your diet for a time. But obviously it is of the greatest help to children.

If you compare the potato with the carrot, then you see it is completely different. You know the potato has haulm but it also has what you eat — the tubers. These are buried in the ground. If one looks at them superficially one might think these tubers are the roots. But this is not so. These tubers are no roots. If you look more closely you will see the roots hanging from the tubers. The real roots are little rootlets which are attached to the tubers, but they fall off easily. When one lifts the potatoes they have already fallen off. But if one lifts them early and carefully they are still there. When we eat the tubers, we have something of the nature of stalk or shoot which only apparently resembles a root. In reality it is a stem or shoot. The leaves are transformed. The potato is therefore something which stands between root and leaf. Because of this it does not contain so many salts as the carrot, it is not so earthly. It grows in the earth but it is not so closely related to the earth. The potato contains mainly carbohydrates, not so many salts, but carbohydrates.

Now you must say to yourselves, when I eat carrots my body can be a real lazy-bones, for only the saliva of the mouth is required to soften the carrot and then only the pepsin of the stomach and so on, and all the important part of the carrot goes to the head. Man needs salts. These are provided by all that is plant root, and particularly by such a root as the carrot.

When someone eats a potato it also goes first into the mouth and then into the stomach and there it is transformed into starch through the effort of the body. Then it passes through the intestines; but in the course of further digestion, in order to get into the blood and from there into the head, it has to be transformed into sugar by a further effort of the body. Only then can it go into the head. So all this needs more effort. You see, if I expend energy on an external object I am that much weaker. This is a secret about man: if I chop wood i.e. expend energy on an outer object, I become fatigued, weaker. If however I expend energy inwardly i.e. transform carbohydrates into starch, and starch into sugar, then I become stronger. If I do this and impregnate myself with sugar by eating potatoes, I become strong. If I expend energy outwardly I lose it. If I use energy inwardly I gain strength. It is not a question of filling oneself up with food but of food developing forces in the body.

So one can say: roots — all roots — are like the carrot, only not in the same degree. They act mainly on the head. Roots give to the body what it needs for itself. Food which tends even a little towards the stem/leaf stage containing carbohydrates gives the body strength needed for work and movement.

Now I have already talked about the potato. Nevertheless the potato weakens man because it uses up *so* much energy. And above all it does not give him strength in the long run. But the principle which I explained to you holds good especially for the potato.

Just as potatoes are an inferior food, so are grains superior — wheat, rye, etc. These also contain carbohydrates but in a form that man can transform into starch and sugar in the best possible way. By means of the carbohydrates in grains he can strengthen himself as far as it is at all possible. Think how strong country people are, simply because they eat a lot of their own bread which is made from grain. They must of course have healthy bodies. Rather coarse bread is the healthiest food, if one can stand it, but you have to have a healthy body. Then through the transformation of starch and sugar the body becomes particularly strong.

Now there are other questions. You see, man, in the course

101

of his development, has, of his own accord, developed the habit of eating grain not in the same way as animals do. The horse eats its oats almost straight from the field. Animals eat their cereals as they come from the field. The birds would be very badly off as regards grain, if they had to wait till somebody came and cooked it for them. Man, of his own accord, took to cooking his cereals. Now what happens when one cooks one's grains? You see, if I cook them, I do not eat them cold but warm. When we inwardly digest our food we expend heat. Without heat it is not possible to transform carbohydrates into starch and starch into sugar. It requires an internal heating up. If I heat food before eating it and make it warm, then I am helping the body. It does not have to expend its own warmth. Firstly, by cooking, the food is involved in a fire or heat process. That is the first thing. The second is that the food is completely transformed. Just think what becomes of flour when I bake it into bread. It is completely changed. But in what way does it become different? First, I must have ground the corn. What does it mean to grind the corn? Make it small, break it up fine. What I do with the grains when I grind them and make them fine, I would have to do in my own body. Everything that I do in this way, I would have to do in my own body. In this way I relieve the body of what it would otherwise have to do. It is the same when I heat the grain. Everything that I do when I cook relieves the body of the task, in as much as I get the food into a condition in which it is easier to digest.

You only have to think of the difference between eating raw potatoes or cooked potatoes. If we would eat raw potatoes, the stomach would have to produce a tremendous lot of heat to transform this potato, which is already on the way to becoming starch. This transformation, however, does not suffice. The potato passes into the intestines. Here also much effort is exerted and yet the potato remains stuck in the intestines. These forces are not adequate to carry the potato into the rest of the body. So, if one eats raw potatoes, either one merely fills one's stomach because the intestines are unable to do anything with them, or one fills up the intestines. But it does not go any further. However, if one prepares the potatoes by cooking, the stomach has less to do, likewise the intestines. The potatoes pass into the blood and so up into the head.

So you see by cooking food, particularly foods rich in carbohydrates, it is possible to aid nutrition.

You know these days there are a lot of foolish ideas around, particularly about diet. They have become a fashion. There are raw-food fanatics who no longer want to cook anything, but eat everything raw. Why is this? Because from materialistic science people do not know how things are, and they do not want to know anything about spiritual science, hence they think up just anything. The whole raw-food idea is nothing but a foolish fantasy. For a time one can boost the body, because it has to exert a lot of energy if one only eats raw food, but it collapses all the more later on.

Now we come to the fats in general. Plants, almost all plants, contain fats — vegetable fats, which they prepare from the mineral kingdom. Fats however are not taken up by the human body as easily as carbohydrates and salts. Salts do not have to be transformed. If you put salt in your soup, this salt finds its way to your head almost unchanged. It goes into your head. When you eat potatoes it is not potatoes that go into your head, but instead, sugar. The transformation takes place in the way I have already told you. But with fats, be they of vegetable or animal origin, it is not so simple. The fats which you eat are almost completely absorbed by the saliva and the digestive juices of the stomach and intestines, and what enters the blood is something entirely different. Man and animal have to create their *own* fats in the intestines and in the blood, through the power engendered by the fats they eat.

You see this is the difference between fats and sugar or salt. Salt and sugar man really takes direct from nature,

103

except that he has to transform into sugar what comes from potatoes, or rye and so on. Still, there is something from nature in it. In the fat in man and animal there is nothing any more that comes from nature. They have made it themselves. But they would not have the power to do so if they did not eat and if the intestines and blood did not need fats. So one can say, man cannot make salts. The human body would never contain salt nor produce it if it did not take it in. If man did not eat carbohydrates, if he did not eat bread or something similar which gives him carbohydrates, he would not be able to make sugar and if he were not able to make sugar, he would forever be a weakling. So gentlemen, be thankful for sugar. You have strength because you are full of sweetness through and through. The moment you were no longer thoroughly impregnated with sweetness, you would have no more strength, you would collapse.

This applies to whole peoples. There are some which do not eat much sugar nor substances which are transformed into sugar. These peoples are weak as regards physical strength. There are others which consume much sugar. They are strong.

With fats things are not so simple. When man or animal has fats in his body, the credit is his, or rather his body's. Fats are entirely his own product. So the fats that he takes in from outside from plant or animal he annihilates and in the overcoming of them he develops strength.

With potatoes, rye or wheat, man develops his strength by transforming them. With the fats that he eats, he develops strength by destroying them. When I destroy something external, I become tired. When however, inside me, I destroy a very fat beefsteak, the destruction of this or of some plant fats, gives me strength to develop my own fat, if my body has that tendency. So you see that fats which are consumed work in the body in quite a different way than do the carbohydrates.

Now my friends, the human body is very complicated and

what I am telling you represents a lot of work. Much has to be done in the body in order for these fats to be annihilated. Let us suppose a man eats the leaves of a plant. That is where the fats are which he gets from the plants. Now, why do you imagine that the stalk is such a tough thing? Because it transforms the leaves so that they become carbohydrates. When the leaves are green – the greener they are the more fatty substance they yield. So if man eats bread he does not get much fat. He obtains from, shall we say, watercress more fat than if he eats bread. Consequently people felt the need to eat their bread with butter, with a little fat, or like country folk, with fat bacon or the like, which is fat. In this way two needs are taken care of. When I eat bread, it goes right up into the head because the root nature of the plant has gone all the way up the stalk, and the stalk has the root forces within it, in spite of the fact that it grows up in the air. The important thing is not whether something is up in the air, but whether it is of a root nature. But the leaf, the green leaf, is not of root nature. Below the surface of the earth, no green leaf appears. The standing corn ripens towards late summer and autumn, when the sun forces are no longer very strong, but the leaf needs the strong forcing power of the sun to mature. It grows towards the sun. This is why its effects are mainly on the lungs and heart, while the root strengthens the head and even the potato is of such a nature that it makes its way into the head. When we eat the leaf which provides us with most vegetable fats, we strengthen our heart and lungs – our chest region. The secret of human nutrition is: If I want to influence my head, I must eat roots, or cereals that grow on stalks, or such like. If I want to influence my heart and lungs, I must eat lettuce, etc. But because these are annihilated in the intestines and only their forces are active, we do not need to do so much cooking and this is why leaves are used for salads. But everything that acts on the head must be cooked and cannot be made into salads. Cooked food works right up into the head.

105

Salads work mainly in building up heart, lungs and so on. They are nourishing owing to their fat content.

Now it is not enough only to support the head and chest region. We also have to build up the metabolic system. We need a stomach, intestines, kidneys and a liver and all these must be maintained. For this man needs protein, the protein in plants, as it is contained in the flower and above all in the fruit. So we can say the root nourishes mainly the head; the leaf, which is in the middle of the plant, nourishes the chest; and what comes from the fruit, the abdomen.

When we see a field of wheat, we can say what a good thing it is that it is there, for it nourishes our head. If we look at the lettuce we are planting and all the leaves we eat that we do not have to cook because they are digested in the intestines and we only need their forces, there we have all we need to maintain our chest organs. But if we look up at the plums, apples and other fruit which grows on trees — well, you see we do not have to do much cooking there, for they have been cooked by the sun the whole summer. Here we have an inner ripening. This is different from what takes place in the root, which is not ripened by the sun, and different from the withering of the stem and so on. We do not need to cook fruits on the whole; only if we have a weak constitution, which is unable to digest the fruit in the intestines, must we cook them, stew them and so on. So if one has anything wrong with the intestines, one must be careful only to take cooked fruit. If one has healthy intestines, fruit is the very thing to strengthen and maintain the lower organs, due to the protein they contain. The protein in fruit builds up our stomach, builds up everything we have as digestive organs in our abdomen.

You see these things used to be know by instinct. People would not have been able to tell you what I have just explained, but they knew it instinctively. This is why they have always eaten a mixed diet of roots, leaves and fruits.

106

They have eaten all these things. They also knew instinctively the right proportions.

But you also know that people do not only eat plants, they also eat meat, fat etc. from animals.

You see, anthroposophy is not fanatical nor sectarian; it just states the facts. One cannot say that people should only eat plants or should eat meat, and so on. One should say instead: There are people who cannot from heredity muster the necessary forces to do all the work required to annihilate vegetable fats in order to produce the capacity to recreate fats in their own body. Those who eat only vegetable fats must either give up the idea of becoming fat fellows, because plant fats have to be destroyed in order to recreate fat, or they must have a very healthy digestive system which can easily annihilate these vegetable fats, and so produce the forces to lay up their own fat. Most people are so made that they cannot produce enough fat if they only digest vegetable fats, but if they eat animal fats or meat, this is not completely annihilated. Vegetable fats do not proceed beyond the intestines. They are annihilated there. Fat contained in meat penetrates further into the human body. Therefore a person can afford to be weaker than if he eats only vegetable fats. There are certain bodies which do not like to eat fat bacon nor other fatty foods. These are bodies which find it easy to annihilate fats and wish to make their own fat. These bodies say: The fat that I carry I want to make myself, I want to have my own fat. If however someone loads his table with fatty foods, then he does not say: I want to make my own fat. Instead he says: The world can give me my fat. The animal fats pass into the body. This facilitates nutrition.

When a child is always after sugar it is not because of its nutritional value. It has nutritional value, but a child does not take it for that reason but because it is sweet. When taking sugar it becomes conscious of its sweetness. When a man eats beef or pork fat, it passes into his body. It gives infinite pleasure to the body just as sugar gives infinite pleasure to the child. It has not the same quality, but the person feels that this pleasure is there. Of course, man needs this inner pleasure for his bodily existence. His body loves meat. One eats meat only if the body loves it.

However we must not be fanatical about these things. There are people who cannot do without eating some meat. One must therefore carefully try it out and see if someone really can live without meat. But if someone can manage without meat, he will feel stronger on changing from meat to vegetarian diet. You see, this is a difficulty. Some people are not able to live without meat, but if a person can do so, he will feel stronger on becoming a vegetarian, because he is not obliged to deposit alien fat, but only makes his own fat. This makes him feel strong. And I can say from personal experience that I could not have stood the strain of the last 24 years in any other way. I could not have travelled the whole night and then given a lecture the following day, and so on. Because, as we said, the work of making a substance for oneself as a vegetarian, is taken away if one lets the animal do it for one. This is how it is. You must not think that in any way I am preaching vegetarianism, for it must always be tried out first to see if a person can become a vegetarian or not. It depends on how he is made.

You see, my friends, this is particularly important as regards protein. One can also transform vegetable protein if one is able to annihilate it in the intestines and one acquires strength in so doing. But if the intestines are weak, one has to get protein from outside, which is then animal protein. Hens that lay eggs are also animals. The role of protein is completely misunderstood when it is not seen from the point of view of spiritual science.

When I eat roots, their salts pass into my head. When I eat lettuce, the forces — not the fats themselves, but the forces which I derive from the fats in the plants — go into my chest, lungs and heart. When I eat fruits the protein in the fruit does not go into the chest but stays in the intestines.

108

Only the protein that comes from animals goes further and supplies the body because it spreads out. So we can say that when a person eats a lot of protein he will be a well-fed man. In this materialistic age this has led the medical world to recommend excessively high-protein diets. It has been maintained that 120-150 grams of protein are necessary. This is rubbish! Today it is known that only a quarter of this is necessary. And really if one eats such a lot of protein which is unnecessary, then it can be like the story of the professor and his assistant. They wanted to feed an under-nourished person with protein. Now one assumes that the protein, if taken in large quantities, will be transformed in the body and that the urine will show that protein has been eaten. Now it happened with this person that the urine did not show that any protein had been digested. The professor was furious! (They did not tumble to it that the protein had passed out through the intestine.) The assistant, with shaking knees suggested: 'Herr Professor — perhaps through the intestine?' What had happened was that they had overfed the person with protein, but it did not do him any good, because the protein went from the stomach into the intestine and so out again. It did not spread into the body. When one eats too much protein it does not go into the body but into the faeces. But he gets something out of it, for before it is excreted it remains for a time in the intestines and becomes toxic and poisons the whole body! That is what one gets from too much protein. This poisoning often leads to arterial sclerosis and many people get arterial sclerosis at an early age simply because they are overfed with protein.

So it is really important to understand the subject of nutrition as I have explained. Most people have the idea that the more one eats the better fed one is. This is not correct. Sometimes one is better maintained if one eats less, because one does not poison oneself.

One must know how the individual substances work. One must know that salts act mainly on the head; carbohydrates,

which are in our staple foods (bread and potatoes) act on the
lungs, throat, palate, and so on; fats act mainly on the heart
and blood vessels — arteries and veins; and protein chiefly
on the lower organs. The head does not get anything much
from protein. The protein in the head — of course there *is*
protein in the head since it consists of living substance —
this protein man must make for himself. So one should not
believe that man gets a particularly healthy brain when he
is overfed, rather the contrary, his brain will be poisoned.

Perhaps I shall have to give another talk on nutrition. That
would be very nice, for these questions are very rewarding.
So, next Saturday at nine o'clock.

Protein   : abdominal organs
Fats   : heart and blood vessels
Carbohydrates: lungs, throat and palate
Salts   : head

NUTRITION AND CHILD NUTRITION
THE DIGESTION OF PROTEIN. ARTERIAL SCLEROSIS

Lecture to the Workmen   Dornach, 2nd August 1924

Today I would like to add something to what was said on Thursday in answer to Herr Burle's question. I explained the four things which are necessary for human nutrition: salts, then what one calls carbohydrates, contained particularly in potatoes but also to a high degree in our field cereals and pulses. Then I said that man needs fats and he needs protein. But I have also explained how different the processes are in man with regard to the digestion of protein and salts for instance. Salt is taken up by the body and reaches the head, remaining as salt. It is dissolved, but not changed in any other way. It retains its forces as salt right into the human head. Whereas protein — the substance contained in the ordinary hen's egg but also in plants — this protein is immediately destroyed in the stomach and intestines. It does not remain protein. In doing this man has used forces to annihilate this protein and the result is that he acquires new forces to reconstitute protein again. And so he creates his own protein. He could not do this if he did not destroy the other protein first.

Let us imagine how it is with this protein. Suppose you have become very clever, so clever that you think you are able to make a clock. But you have only seen a clock from outside. Well, you will not be able to make a clock straight away. But if you risk taking it to pieces, and can remember how the individual bits fit together, then you learn from taking it to pieces, how to put it together again. This is what the human body does with protein. The protein that

111

man takes in, he completely takes to pieces. Protein consists of carbon, nitrogen, oxygen, hydrogen and sulphur. These are the principle constituents of protein. The protein is broken up into its constituent parts so that man no longer has protein when the stuff gets into the intestines, but carbon, nitrogen, oxygen, hydrogen and sulphur. You see man has taken the protein to pieces as one does a clock. You will say: Yes, but if one has once taken a clock to pieces, one can remember how it is put together and one can make many more clocks, therefore one need only eat protein once and one will be able to make it over and over again. This however is not so, for man as a whole entity has a memory, but his body as such has not got the kind of memory that can remember this sort of thing. The body uses the forces for the reconstitution, hence we must always eat protein in order to make protein.

Now man does something very, very complicated when he makes his own protein. He first takes it to pieces. In this way the carbon gets into his body everywhere. But you know we also get oxygen from the air. This combines with the carbon we have in us, which we have got from protein and other foods. We combine some of this carbon with the oxygen we have breathed in to make our own protein. The oxygen from the protein we have eaten we do not retain. We breathe it out with the remainder of the carbon as carbon dioxide. We do not build the protein in our own body in the way that materialists imagine. They think that if we eat a lot of eggs they are distributed throughout our body. This is not so. The organisation of our body prevents us from becoming stupid hens when we eat eggs. Of course, we do not become hens, for we destroy the protein in our intestines. In place of the oxygen in the protein, we take oxygen from the air, with the oxygen we also breathe in nitrogen because it too is always in the air. Again, the nitrogen from the egg we do not use, instead we use the nitrogen from the air. The hydrogen from the egg we use least of all. We use the

112

hydrogen which we take in through the nose, through the ears and altogether through our senses. We use *this* hydrogen to make our own protein. Sulphur we get continually from the air. From the protein that we eat we only retain the carbon, the rest we take from the air.

So you see this is how it is with protein and it is somewhat similar with regard to fats. We make our own protein and use only the carbon from the alien protein. We also make our own fat and use only a very little of the nitrogen that we take in with our food. So we produce our own protein and our own fats. Only what we eat as potatoes, pulses and cereals makes its way into the body — not completely one may say, only as far as the lower parts of the head. What we get from salts, that passes into the whole head and from this we make what we need for our bones.

So you see, my friends, because of this we must see to it that our body receives healthy plant protein. Our body gets a lot from healthy plant protein. When you eat protein in eggs, your body can be lazy — really lazy. It is easy for the body to break it up. Plant protein, as we get it from fruit is particularly valuable for us. For anyone who wants to keep healthy it is necessary to eat fruit, either raw or cooked. He must have fruit. If someone avoids eating any fruit he will gradually develop a very sluggish digestion.

But you must also grow the plants in the right way. You must realise that plants are living things. They are not minerals, they are alive. A plant comes from a seed which we put into the soil. The plant cannot flourish if one does not enliven the soil a bit. And how does one do this? One enlivens it by proper manuring. So, it is proper manuring which yields the good plant protein we need.

Here again we must consider that for centuries man knew that the right manure comes from the cow-shed, pig-sty and so on. The right manure is what comes from the farm. But in recent times, when everything became materialistic, people said: Well, we can find out what substances are in the manure and then take them from the mineral kingdom — artificial fertilisers.

If we use mineral fertilisers it is like putting salts into the soil, only the root becomes strong. We only get from the plant what forms and maintains our bones. We do not get a proper protein. This is why our crops suffer from protein deficiency, and it will become more and more so if people do not revert to proper manuring.

There have been conferences of farmers where the farmers have said: Crops are becoming worse and worse. This is true, but they did not know why. Older people know that in their youth, the fruits of the field were of better quality. One must not conclude that one can synthesise fertiliser from the substances found in cow-dung. One must realise that cow-dung (which does not come from a chemical laboratory but from the very much more scientific laboratory within the cow itself) is the substance which does not only strengthen the root of the plant but works strongly right up into the fruit and produces proper protein in the plants which makes man strong when he eats it.

If you always manure with mineral fertilisers, as people so like to do these days, or, even worse, with nitrogen produced from the air, then your children and even more your children's children, will have very pale faces. You will not be able to distinguish the colour of the face from the hands, if the hands are white. A fresh and healthy complexion depends on manuring the fields in the right way.

So you see, when one speaks about nutrition, one must take into account how the food is produced. This is extremely important. Various circumstances can show that the human body is bound to demand what it needs. Prisoners who are sentenced to years of imprisonment usually get food which is deficient in fat. They develop a terrible craving for fat. If the warden comes into the cell with a candle and some of the grease drops on the floor, they immediately bend down and pick it up and eat it because the body has a tremendous craving for any food it needs and of which it is deprived. This is not noticeable when one eats proper food every day. If the body gets what it needs it does not miss anything but if something is lacking for weeks on end then the body starts craving for it. This must be added to what we have said.

I have already told you that many other things have changed as well as manuring. Our forbears in Europe in the 12th and 13th centuries and even earlier were in many ways different from us. This is not usually taken into account. And among the many things which were different, was the fact that they did not get any potatoes to eat. Potatoes were introduced later. Eating potatoes has had a great influence on man. You see, if you eat cereals, the lungs and heart are strengthened. They make lungs and heart strong. In this way man develops a healthy chest and he is well. He is not so keen on thinking, but rather on breathing, for instance. His breathing can stand a lot. You must not imagine that these people are strong in their breathing who are continually opening the window and screaming for fresh air and so on, but the strong ones are those whose organisation is such that they can stand any kind of air. People who cannot bear something are not the hardy ones. The hardy ones are those that can stand any conditions.

In these days there is much talk about hardening off. Think of what is done to children. Children — mainly those of well-to-do parents but also others now follow suit more and more — are dressed like this: Whereas we in our youth wore proper stockings and were fully clothed except perhaps we had bare feet, now children's clothes barely reach the knees or are even shorter. If people only knew that this involves the greatest danger of developing appendicitis later, they would think again. But fashion is so tyrannical that other points of view are ignored. At present children's clothes only reach to their knees or less and it will come about that they will barely cover their stomachs. That

115

too will become the fashion. Fashion is extraordinarily compelling!

But what is of real importance, people do not even notice. What is important is that man's organisation is so well ordered that it allows him to digest all the food he eats. I think it is really important that one knows that man becomes strong when he can digest properly what he takes in. He is not made hardy by being treated in his childhood as I have told you. Children are so hardened off that when later on — just look at them — they are crossing the road in scorching heat, they are dripping wet and nearly collapse. To be hardened off does not make one hardy. Really hardy people can stand anything. In former times people were not hardened off much, but they had healthy lungs, healthy hearts and so on.

Now the potato arrived and it became a major food. The potato hardly helps the heart and lungs. It goes straight up into the head — not to the upper part, only to the lower part, which is the seat of critical thinking. This is why in pre-potato times there were fewer journalists. Printing was not yet invented. Imagine how much thinking goes on today, just to fill the newspaper! All this thinking, which is quite unnecessary — there is far too much of it! For all this thinking we have to thank the potato! When a person eats potatoes he is continually stimulated to think. He cannot help thinking. Consequently his lungs and heart become weak. Consumption only became widespread after the introduction of the potato. The weakest constitutions are found in areas where the potato is grown and eaten almost exclusively.

It is spiritual science which, as I have often told you, can get to know the material aspect of things. Materialistic science knows nothing of nutrition, it does not know what is healthy for man. This is the peculiarity of materialism: it thinks, thinks, thinks, and knows nothing. If one wants to stand fair and square in life, one must *know* something. These are some of the things I wanted to tell you about nutrition.

116

* * * * *

Now if there is anything further you would like to know, perhaps you would ask some questions.

Question:
Herr Doktor spoke last time about arterial sclerosis. It is generally assumed that this is caused through eating a lot of meat, eggs, etc. I know someone who developed arterial sclerosis at the age of 50 and became stiff up to the age of 70. Now this person is 85 or 86 and is today more active and vigorous than he was at 50 or 60. Has the arterial sclerosis receded? Is this possible or what else could be the reason? This person never smoked, did not drink much alcohol and was moderate in his way of living. But in his younger days he ate rather a lot of meat. At the age of 70 he could only do very little work, but today at 85 or 86 he is constantly active. He is still alive.

Rudolf Steiner:
Well, you say it was a person who at 50 developed arterial sclerosis, became stiff and incapable of much work. I do not know if his memory also suffered. You probably did not notice this. This condition remained into his seventies, then he again became active and vigorous and is still living. Is there anything noticeable today that reminds one of arterial sclerosis? Or is he really vigorous and free in his movements?

Questioner:
He is really vigorous and freer in his movements than when he was 65 or 70. He is my father!

Rudolf Steiner:
First one would have to find out what kind of arterial sclerosis it was, for you see usually it sets in in the arteries all over the body. If all the arteries are sclerotic then a person's

117

soul and spirit are no longer in command of the body. The body becomes stiff. But now let us assume that the sclerosis is not in the whole of the body but that the brain remains unaffected. Then we have the following: You see I know something about *your* state of health. Perhaps there is a certain parallel with your father — I do not know him. You suffer or did suffer — I hope it will be completely cured — from hay fever. This shows that you have something in you which the body can only develop when it does not have a tendency to sclerosis in the head but only in the other parts of the body. No one who has a tendency towards sclerosis in the whole body can develop hay fever. Hay fever is the very opposite of arterial sclerosis. You suffer from hay fever. Your hay fever is something like a safety valve against sclerosis. (Obviously it is not very good to have hay fever, it is better if it is cured, but the tendency is what matters.)

But everyone gets arterial sclerosis to a certain extent. One cannot get old without it. If one gets it in the whole body one is helpless. One becomes stiff all over. If however one gets arterial sclerosis in the head but not in the rest of the body, and one gets very old then the etheric body, of which I have spoken, becomes stronger and stronger. Then the etheric body no longer needs the brain so much, so this can become old and stiff. The etheric body will be able to control the sclerosis which previously made a person old and stiff. It is then not so bad and one can manage to control it.

Your father may not necessarily have had hay fever, but can have had the tendency, and it might be this tendency which is helping him now. One can even say, though it goes a bit against the grain, that there can be someone with a tendency to hay fever and he may say: Thank God that I have got this tendency; I have not actually got hay fever, but it gives me at the same time the tendency to keep my blood vessels supple. If hay fever remains only a tendency it is a protection against sclerosis. But if this person has a son, he may develop what his father had

118

inwardly as a tendency. In the son it can manifest itself as a disease.

These are the mysteries of heredity. What was outwardly healthy in the forefathers becomes an illness in the progeny. People classify diseases, speak of arterial sclerosis, pulmonary tuberculosis, cirrhosis of the liver, stomach upsets and so on. They can be written down nicely in a book, one after the other; they can be described, but it does not do much good, for the simple reason that arterial sclerosis is different in every person. No two people have the same sort of arterial sclerosis. Everybody gets it in a different way. That is how it is, my friends, and it is not surprising.

Once there were two professors at Berlin university. One was 70 years old and the other 90. The 70 year old was a very famous man. He had written many books, but lived with his philosophy steeped in materialism. His thoughts were stuck in materialism and he developed arterial sclerosis. So at 70 he was obliged to retire. The 90 year old, his colleague, was not a materialist but remained like a child throughout most of his life and was still a very vivacious lecturer at 90. He said: 'I cannot understand my colleague, a mere youngster! I do not want to retire yet. I feel very young.' The other was done for — the 'youngster'! He could no longer lecture. Obviously the one who was 90 was also sclerotic. His arteries were calcified but his mind and soul were so flexible that he could still do something with them. The other one was quite unable to do anything.

Now something further on Herr Burle's question about carrots. He said: 'The human body demands what it needs by its own instincts. Children are often seen with a carrot in their hand. Children and adults are sometimes forced to eat food which is not good for them. I think one should not do this if someone has an antipathy against certain foods. I have a boy who does not like potatoes.'

Well, you need only call to mind one thing. If animals did not have an instinct for what is good for them and what

119

is not, they would have died out long ago because there are always poisonous plants among the herbage in meadows. If they did not know for certain that they must not eat poisonous plants, they would eat them. And yet they always pass them by! But there are other things. Animals select carefully what is good for them. Have you ever force-fed geese? Do you think the geese would do that of their own accord? It is people who force so much into the geese. With pigs of course it is a little different. But imagine what lean pigs we would have if they were not obliged to eat so much. But with pigs it is somewhat different. They have acquired a hereditary tendency since their ancestors have been accustomed to eat things which made them fat. These things were put into their food. The original pigs had to be forced to eat them. No animal of its own accord eats what it does not want. But what has materialism done? Obviously it does not believe in such instincts.

You see, I had a friend, a friend of my youth, and when we were together, we were fairly sensible over what we ate — we often ate together as young people. We ordered what people usually ate and what one thought was good for one. Well, our lives drifted apart, but after many years I returned to the town where he lived and was invited to lunch. And what did I see? At the side of his plate was a pair of scales. I asked him what he was doing with the scales. Of course I knew, but I wanted to hear what he would say. He answered: 'I weigh the amount of meat and salad that is right for me and will do me good.' So he weighed everything that was to go on his plate because science ordained it! But what had he really done? He had weaned himself from all instincts and in the end had no idea what he should eat. You see it said in the book, a person needs 120-150 grams of protein (today it says one only needs 50 grams). This he conscientiously weighed out! It was all the wrong thing to do.

Of course in the case of diabetes it is quite different. This is obvious, since the disease of diabetes is evidence that a man has lost his instinct for food.

It is a fact that if a child has a tendency, even a slight tendency, to worms, it will go to considerable lengths to get what it wants. You will sometimes be surprised to see how such a child will find a field where there are carrots and there it will be, eating them. Even if the field is far away, the child will run to it, because a child with a tendency to worms has a longing to eat carrots. So the wisest thing to do is to observe what a little child likes or does not like to eat, after it is weaned. When the young child first begins to eat, one can learn from it what man should eat. If one first forces the young child to eat what one thinks it ought to eat, the instincts become lost. One should be guided by the young child's instinct. Obviously one must curb what might become a bad habit, but one has to be observant all the time.

Take for instance a child who, in spite of your having given it everything which as far as you know it needs, yet when for the first time it comes to table for a meal, cannot resist climbing on a chair and stretching across the table to pinch a lump of sugar. Now you must take this in the right way, for a child who climbs on a chair to sneak a lump of sugar has almost certainly something wrong with its liver. The fact that a child pinches sugar shows that there is something not quite in order with the liver. Only children which have something wrong with their liver — which can be cured by the sugar — only they pinch sugar. Others have no interest in sugar, they leave it alone. Of course this must not be allowed to become a bad habit, but one must understand why it does it. There are two aspects to consider.

You see, if a child watches all the time to see when father and mother are not looking so that it can take the sugar, then later on the child will take other things. If, however, one gives the child what it craves, it will not become a thief. Thus it is also morally important that one observes these things. It is very important. So we must answer your question in this way: One must observe what the little child wants and what it refuses, and not force it to take what it rejects. If for instance, as happens very often, the child does not want to eat meat, it is because this would leave poisonous residues in the intestines and the child tries to avoid it. It has this instinct. A child who sits at table where everyone is eating meat and yet refuses it, has a tendency to develop poisonous residues in its intestines from meat. One must take all this into consideration.

From this you see that science must become more perceptive. Science today is like a coarse-meshed net. Too much slips through. With only scales and other laboratory techniques it is not really possible to pursue science.

As regards this subject of nutrition which so interests you, one must really understand how this nutrition is intimately connected with the spirit. Often, when people ask such questions, I give two examples. Think of a journalist, he must think such a lot, (albeit usually unnecessarily). He must think so much that no one could really produce so many logical thoughts. You will find that a journalist or anyone whose profession is to write a lot, instinctively likes coffee. He sits in a coffee house, drinking one cup after another, chewing his pen to get something out of it that he can write down. Chewing the pen does not help but the coffee helps one thought to follow another, for each thought has to join on to the last.

But you see, if each thought connects with the previous one, if each one follows the other, this is no good for diplomats. If diplomatists are logical, one finds them boring. They must be entertaining. In society it does not go down well — first, second, third. 'The first was so, the second so, therefore the third and fourth are so; and if the first and second were not, then the third and fourth could never be.' (Faust). It does not go down well if somebody is so logical. As a journalist, one cannot include unrelated matter in a financial article but as a diplomatist one can talk of

122

night clubs, and immediately afterwards of the economy of the country X, then the hair style of Mrs. So-and-so, from which one can pass to the productivity of the colonies, which is the best horse to back, and so on. One must be able to jump from one thought to another. If one wants to become a social success, one develops the instinct to drink a lot of tea. Tea scatters the thoughts. They leap about. Coffee makes one thought follow another. If one wants to flit from thought to thought, one should drink tea. At a diplomatic tea party, (for so it is even called) one drinks tea. The journalist sits in the coffee house and drinks one cup of coffee after another. This shows you what an influence a food or a stimulant has upon thinking. Coffee and tea are of course extreme examples, but they show that one should observe these things. This is very important.

19

POTATOES

Extract from a
Lecture to the Workmen   Dornach, 20th September 1924

Now the potato. If today a scientist or doctor is asked what the potato does when it is eaten — what does he do? You know the potato has become a major food, and in some areas it is quite difficult to prevent people eating potatoes almost exclusively. What does the scientist do when he tests the food value of the potato? He determines the substances present in the potato. Obviously one can do this in a laboratory. One finds carbohydrates. They consist of carbon, oxygen and hydrogen arranged in a particular way. One manages to understand that they are transformed in the human body and become a kind of sugar. But that is as far as one gets. And one cannot get any further. You see, if one feeds an animal with milk, it can, under certain circumstances, thrive quite well, but if one analyses the milk and gives the animal not milk, but its chemical constituents, the animal will die. Why is this? It is because there is something else that works in the milk besides its chemical constituents. Likewise in the potato. This is its spiritual part. Everywhere in nature the spirit works. If from a spiritual point of view one investigates the potato and how it feeds man, one finds that the potato is not fully digested in the digestive tract. It goes through the lymph glands and through the blood and so into the head. In the case of the potato the head has to serve as a digestive organ. If one eats a lot of potatoes the head becomes, so to speak, a stomach. It helps digest.

A food like the potato is very different from wholesome bread for instance. If one eats good bread one digests all the substances of the grain, of the rye and wheat, in a healthy manner in the digestive tract. The result is that the head only receives the spiritual part of the rye and wheat, which is right for it.

One sees that in recent times mankind has been ruined by the eating of potatoes. In fact the potato has contributed considerably to the general poor health of the last few centuries.

20

NUTRITION FROM THE AIR

Extract from a
Lecture to the Workmen   Dornach, 24th September 1924

Now what do you eat? We will look at the individual substances that man eats in his food. The first thing is protein. This is not only found in eggs but in other things — animals and plants. He eats fats and carbohydrates, for instance potatoes, and he eats salts. All other things are compound substances. They are substances which we get from the earth. They are completely dependent on the earth. What we take in through our mouth comes from the earth. But we do not take everything in through the mouth; we also breathe. We take up substances from the air through our breathing. It is normally said that man breathes in oxygen and breathes out carbon dioxide — as if man only breathed in and out, in and out. But this is not true, for what we breathe in contains very finely dispersed food substances. We do not only live by what we eat but also by the finely dispersed substances in the air which we breathe in. If we depended solely on eating we would have to renew our body very frequently. For what we eat is very quickly transformed in the body. Think for instance what trouble it causes, if what should be excreted is not got rid of after 24 hours. What is eaten and excreted passes through a quick process. Renewal of the body would not take 7 or 8 years if we were only to live from what we eat. But because we absorb very finely distributed substances from the air and this proceeds slowly, the renewal spreads over seven or eight years.

It is very important to know that man takes in nutritive substances from the air, because if one now sets to work scientifically in the right way, one finds that the food man eats he uses to renew his head continually. But the substance that man needs to grow nails, shall we say, this he does not get from what he eats, but from the nutritive substances in the air! So we are nourished by eating and nourished by the air we breathe in.

But the thing is that if we take in nourishment by breathing we also take in from surrounding space the soul element, not merely the substance. The substance is so finely dispersed that everywhere the soul element is interwoven, it lives in it. So we can say: Man takes in what pertains to the body with food. The soul element he takes in and lives with it through breathing. But we do not take in a bit of soul with every breath and exhale a bit of soul every time we breathe out. In this case we would cast off our soul. But with our first breath we take in the soul element which from then on maintains our breathing until with our last breath, we free it and it can return to the spiritual world.

PART II

(a) From Lectures given to Members of the Anthroposophical
Society.
(b) From Lectures on Education.
(c) From Medical Lectures & Writings.

21

DIGESTION AND THINKING
DIGESTION AND VEGETARIANISM

Extracts from:
Ernährungsfragen und Heilmethoden   22nd October 1906

Digestion and Thinking.

A certain connection exists between what one calls digestion
and what one calls thinking. In other words, what digestion
is on a lower level, thinking is on a higher. Both stand in
intimate contact in man's organism as he lives in the physical
world. We will give you a concrete example. Logical thinking,
the ability to let one thought proceed from another, is part
of our thinking activity. This logical thinking is something
quite special. One can do certain exercises to direct one's
thinking along certain lines. What this thinking does to your
mind and soul when you carry out these logical exercises,
a certain substance does to your digestion — namely coffee.
This is no fantastic assumption; one can verify this fact. What
you impose on your stomach with coffee, you bring about
in your thinking when you practise exercises in logical
thinking. When you drink coffee you promote, in a certain
way, the correct succession of thoughts. And when one says
that drinking coffee brings about an enhancement of that
activity which is necessary for the strengthening of one's
thinking, this is correct. But coffee does not further logical
thinking in an independent way, it acts compulsively. You
feel a certain dependence, something like an effect from
outside. If a person wants to think logically but not independently he should drink a lot of coffee. If however he
wants to do the thinking himself, then he must abstain from

128

what works on the lower organism, he must develop the forces of his own soul. Then he will find that after the appropriate exercises the stomach will get right or remain right.

A further point; in contrast to logical thinking there is that thinking which cannot for a moment remain with one thought — uncontrolled thinking. It has a dissipating effect and finds expression in the fact that one thought does not connect with the next. This thinking is correlated with the effect of a certain substance on the digestion and this is contained in tea. Tea actually works in the lower organism as flighty thinking in the upper. From this you can deduce that the effect of tea can, under certain circumstances, be rather devastating. However you need not think that someone who has drunk tea all his life will in the end be inwardly torn to pieces. If tea has not affected him in this detrimental way, this only goes to show that his organism possesses sufficient resistance.

Digestion and Vegetarianism.
One has to be clear about the fact that humanity will have to become more and more conscious of questions concerning diet, but people who collect material about nutrition very often make a particular mistake. This is that man wants to learn too much from what he calls 'Nature'. He wants to follow Nature in every respect. Paracelsus says on the contrary: 'One should not be a slave to Nature. The doctor should indeed go through the curriculum of Nature but he should be an artist, he must continue the processes of Nature.' Paracelsus sees the real remedies not in the finished products taken from Nature but in new products which will be created in accord with the spirit of Nature. Paracelsus anticipates a new epoch of medicine in which these new products will be used as effective remedies. This is what is meant by continuing the processes of Nature.

When people today want to prove that a mixed diet is best for man, their argument is: Ruminants are plant-eaters, they have a specially adapted stomach and digestive apparatus. Beasts of prey are meat-eaters, their digestive tract and teeth are adapted to eating meat. Man's teeth and digestive tract are intermediate between the two. Therefore Nature herself shows that man should have a mixed diet. But everything in the world is in flux, in becoming and growing. It is not how man appears today but how he can become different that matters. If he would change over to a vegetarian diet, then the organs more adapted to meat-eating would regress and those necessary for vegetarian diet would be developed. One has to take into consideration how it was in the past and what it can become in the future. One does not give man the right food if one bases it on his present condition but only if one considers his future inner development. Statistics only give outer facts, they do not take into account the direction in which humanity should proceed. One must really look at the world with a wider view.

Now picture to yourself the character of the Russian peasant as it is today [1906] and then that of the Englishman. The Russian peasant puts as little emphasis on his ego as possible. It is the opposite with the Englishman. This is even apparent in the written word. The Englishman uses a capital letter for 'I'. If one looks further one finds that the Englishman eats five times as much sugar as the Russian. So here we find again the connection between digestion and thinking. What happens in the digestive system through eating large quantities of sugar has it counterpart in the upper part of man in an increased independence in thinking.

Now you can imagine that in these circumstances one can sometimes act correctively. A person could arrange his diet so that he only needs a very short time for digestion, whereas another might take a long time. This affords us a deep insight into the human organism. If one person eats rice and his digestion is finished quickly then certain forces remain over which are available for him to use for thinking. Another person who eats, for instance, wild duck and requires a correspondingly longer time for digestion can be quite a clever man but the thoughts produced really come from his stomach! The first one may be a poor thinker but his thinking will be independent, whereas the other may be a vigorous thinker but his thinking will not be independent. From this we can learn a lesson.

Now to turn to another subject: The greatest care must be taken that the body does not get too much nor too little protein. It is imperative to find the right quantity, because, in our digestion, protein corresponds to that which in our thinking activity produces mental images. The same activity which produces fruitful thinking is engendered in the lower organism by protein. If the intake of protein is excessive a superabundance of forces is produced which, in the lower organism, corresponds to the forming of images in the upper. Now man should become more and more master of his mental images. Therefore the intake of protein should remain within certain limits, otherwise man will be overwhelmed by his mental images from which he should gradually become free: This is what Pythagoras had in mind when he instructed his pupils to: 'Refrain from beans'.

Of course people will say: Look at that rice-eater, he is a poor thinker. Yes, but then undoubtedly this man with his rice is not yet very far developed. It is not a question of knowing the rules and merely following them in the belief that they will necessarily lead to the desired results. If the upper and the lower do not correspond it can cause trouble. Let us take a person who has recently become a vegetarian. In this new vegetarian the activity in his lower organism will work in a certain way. Certain forces will be changed from material ones into spiritual ones. If however they are not used, they will work in a detrimental way and can even impair the activity of the brain. If such a person works in a bank or is an ordinary intellectual he can do himself great harm unless he can take in spiritual ideas with the forces which have become available through his vegetarian mode of life. So the person who becomes a vegetarian must change to a more spiritual life, otherwise it were better he keep to meat. His memory could become impaired, certain parts of his brain could be impaired, etc. It does not suffice to eat nothing but fruit in the hope that thereby the highest regions of the spiritual life will be unlocked!

* * * * *

22

VEGETARIAN AND MEAT DIETS. MILK. ALCOHOL

Extract from:
Ernährungsfragen im Licht der Geisteswissenschaft
Berlin, 17th December 1908

Sunlight and man's astral body stand in a certain sense as opposites.... This astral body is a spiritual light body. It is the opposite of the outer light. Imagine that the sunlight becomes ever weaker till it is extinguished, and let it go on further still, let it become negative; then you have inner light. And this inner light has the opposite task of outer light which builds up the plant body out of inorganic materials. The inner light, that introduces the partially destructive process which alone makes consciousness possible, raises man to a stage above the plant which he eats, because the plant process is transformed into an opposite process. Thus man, by means of his inner light, stands in a certain way, opposite to the plant....

Let us take the relationship of man to plant when he eats it. He produces in himself, as part of the whole world process, a continuation of the plant. What is produced with the help of sunlight is continually destroyed by the astral body, but thereby it integrates the nervous system into man, thus raising life to consciousness. The astral body, through being a negative light body, is thus the opposite pole to the plant world. This building up process of the plant organism has a spiritual foundation, for spiritual science shows us again and again that what appears to us as light is only the outer expression of something spiritual. Through light something spiritual flows towards us continually, the light of spiritual beings flows towards us. What is concealed behind this physical light is what appears distributed in part also in the astral body. Outwardly, in sunlight, it appears in its physical form; in the astral body it appears in astral form. The spiritual in light works inwardly in us in the building up of our nervous system. In this wonderful way does plant life and human life work together.

Let us now take man's relationship to the animal world when he eats meat. Then things are quite different. In the creature from which he takes his food the process is in a certain way already completed. What he takes fresh from the innocent plant has been already partially transformed and prepared in the animal; for the animal also has an astral body and nervous system. So man absorbs something that does not come to him in its virgin freshness, but something that has gone through a process, something that has already taken in astral forces. What lives in the animal has already developed astral forces in itself. Now one might think that in this way man would have less work to do. This however is not quite true. Supposing I want to build a house out of certain materials. I select the basic materials and can then build the house exactly as I originally intended. But supposing three or four other people have already made parts of it and then I am supposed to make a whole out of it all. Would that make it easier for me? No, certainly not. You can read everywhere in the relevant literature that man's work is facilitated if he uses what is already prefabricated. But man will become a more flexible independent being if he uses primary basic materials of his own choice.

The animal prepares substances in a less complete way. What is thus taken in by man continues to work according to what the astral body of the animal has done to it, and this man has first to overcome. But because a process has already been started by the astral body of a conscious being, therefore man gets something in his organism that affects his nervous system.

This is the fundamental difference between food from the

plant world and food from the animal kingdom. Food from animals acts in a quite specific way on the nervous system and thus on the astral body. But with vegetarian food the nervous system remains undisturbed by anything from outside. Man is then solely responsible for his nervous system. Extraneous products do not penetrate the working of his nerves but only what originates in himself. Those who know how much in the human organism depends on the nervous system will understand what this means. When a person builds up his own nervous system it is sensitive to what comes to him from the spiritual world. It is thanks to food from the plant world that a person can survey the wider interconnections of things, which raises him above prejudices springing from the narrow limits of his personal self. Wherever a person, free and untrammeled, governs his life and thought in accordance with the wider issues, he can thank the plant world for his quick grasp of the situation. Where a person allows himself to give way to temper, antipathy and prejudice, it is owing to food from the animal kingdom.

We are not here making propaganda for vegetarianism. On the contrary, animal food was, for a time, necessary for man and is often still necessary today, because man must stand firmly on the earth and be well embedded in what is personal. Everything that has led man to personal interests is connected with meat eating. The fact that there have been men who have made war, who have had sympathies and antipathies and sensual desires for each other is due to eating meat. But when a person does not act out of narrow self-interest but can grasp the wider perspectives, he owes this to his connection with the plant world through food. Thus certain peoples who are mainly vegetarian have more of a leaning towards spiritual matters, while other peoples develop more bravery, courage and heroism which are also necessary in life. These qualities are not conceivable without the personal element and this is not possible without meat.

135

We are speaking today from a very general human point of view on these questions but we want to make it quite clear that a person can turn in one direction or another and can submerge himself in his personal interests through eating meat. In this way his mind can become dulled as regards the wider issues of existence. One does not usually realise that nutrition is at the root of it when someone says: Now I really don't know how I shall do this or that; I wonder how has he done it? This impossibility of seeing the whole pattern of interconnections is due to nutrition. Compare this with someone who *can* view the overall connections. You can look back on the diet of this person and perhaps also on the diet of his ancestors. A person who, through his ancestors, has an unspoilt nervous system is quite different. He has a different sense for the wider issues of life. One generation can often not destroy the foundation that the ancestors have laid. . . .

It will be a step forward when man, if he is not able to produce his protein requirements in himself, will restrict himself to what in animal food is not permeated by emotions and desires — namely milk. Plant food will take an ever larger place in human nutrition.

As regards individual foods, one can highlight certain advantages regarding vegetarian diet. When a person gets his protein from a vegetarian diet which requires harder work, he develops forces which invigorate his nervous system. Much of what mankind would experience if meat-eating predominated could be avoided by consuming mainly plant foods. We can see how differently vegetarian and meat diets work from the following example. If we look at the physical process under the influence of a meat diet we find that the red blood corpuscles become darker and heavier and the blood has a greater tendency to clot. Phosphates and salts are produced more easily. With predominantly vegetarian food the sedimentation rate of the blood corpuscles is much lower. It is possible for man to prevent his blood becoming very dark. By this means he will be able to control the course of his thinking from his ego, while heavy blood is a sign that he is slavishly given over to what is embedded in his astral body through meat eating.... Connection with the plant world strengthens man inwardly. Meat introduces something which gradually becomes real foreign substance and goes its own independent way in him. This is avoided when the diet is mainly vegetarian. When substances take an independent course in us they bring into play forces which encourage hysterical and epileptic conditions. Because the nervous system is thus influenced from outside it becomes subject to various nervous diseases. So we see that in a certain sense 'Man is what he eats'.

One could enter far more into details but two examples will show that we should not be one-sided. An extreme vegetarian would say that we must not take milk, butter and cheese. But in the production of milk it is mainly the animal's etheric body which is involved. The astral body has hardly anything to do with it. In the early part of his life, as a baby, man can live on milk alone. Everything that he needs is in it. In the production of milk only the fringe of the astral body is involved. If, in old age, one lives mainly on milk, even entirely on milk, a very special effect is produced. Since the person then takes in nothing that can influence his astral body and since in milk he takes something that is already prepared, he is able to develop special forces in his etheric body which can act as powers of healing on his fellow man. For healers wishing to treat their fellow men a milk diet can be of particular assistance.

On the other hand we will describe the effect of another product of the plant world — alcohol. This has a special significance. It arises when the plant process (that occurs through the wonderful influence of light, of which the astral body is the opposite) has ceased. Then a process begins which takes place on a lower level and which is even more injurious to man than eating meat. Man normally conveys substances as far as his astral body and by means of the astral body gives them a particular structure. When however, what is brought to the astral body is broken up by alcohol, then what should take place through the astral body takes place without the astral body and acts directly on the ego and the blood. The effect of alcohol is that what should be done by the free decision of the ego is done by the alcohol. In a certain way it is true that a person who drinks alcohol needs less food. He allows his blood to be penetrated by the forces of alcohol. He hands over to something foreign what he should do himself. In a certain sense one can say that in such a person it is the alcohol that thinks and feels. To the extent that a person relinquishes to alcohol what his ego should rule, he puts himself under the compulsion of something outside himself. He creates for himself a materialistic ego. A person can say: I feel that my ego is enlivened in this way. Yes, certainly, but it is not he but something else to which he has relinquished his ego.

Thus we can show in many ways how, more and more, man can become what he consumes. But spiritual science can also show us how man can become free from the powers of food.

23

PROBLEMS OF NUTRITION
VEGETARIAN AND MEAT DIETS

Lecture. Munich, 8th January 1909
Translated by Maria St. Goar.

In the past I have spoken here on a variety of subjects concerning spiritual life. It may be permissible today, therefore, for me to touch upon a more prosaic theme from the standpoint of spiritual science. Problems of nutrition undoubtedly offer a more mundane subject than many we have heard here. It will be seen, however, that particularly in our age spiritual science has something to say even concerning questions that directly affect everyday life.

On the one hand, spiritual science stands accused, by those who know it only from the outside, of aspiring too loftily to spiritual realms, thus losing the firm ground under its feet. On the other hand, the opposite can perhaps also be heard — again from those who have become acquainted with spiritual science or anthroposophy through only a single lecture or brochure. This consists in the statement than anthroposophists are entirely too concerned with, and talk too much about, questions of what they should eat and drink. In some respects these critics might well be called idealists in that they believe they view the common aspects of life from a certain exalted level. They raise this objection particularly by taking a stand that can be expressed in the following way. 'What man eats and drinks is unimportant. It does not matter what food one takes, rather must one rise above the material dimension by the strength of one's spirit.' Even a well-intentioned idealist might level this objection against anthroposophists.

Well, at a time when these questions are being widely discussed from other angles, it might be interesting to hear what spiritual science has to say about them.

It was a German philosopher, Ludwig Andreas Feuerbach, to whom the phrase, 'A man is what he eats,' is attributed. Many thinkers of consequence have agreed with Feuerbach that what man produces is basically the result of foods ingested by him and his actions are influenced by the food absorbed in a purely materialistic way through his digestion. With so much discussion of eating going on, somebody might get it into his head to believe that man is indeed physically nothing more than what he eats. Now, we shall have several things to say on this point.

We must understand each other precisely as to the purpose of today's lecture and the intention behind it. We are not agitating in favour of particular tendencies, nor are we trying to be reformative. The spiritual scientist is obliged to state the truth of things. His attitude must never be agitatorial, and he must be confident that when a person has perceived the truth of what he says, he will then proceed to do the right thing. What I have to say, therefore, does not recommend one course as opposed to another, and he who assumes that it does will misunderstand it completely. Merely the facts will be stated, and you will have understood me correctly if you realise that I am not speaking for or against anything.

Bearing this in mind, we can raise the question from the standpoint of spiritual science as to whether the statement, 'A man is what he eats,' does not have a certain justification after all. We must continually bear in mind that the body of man is the tool of the spirit. In discussing the various functions the body has to perform, we see that man utilises it as a physical instrument. An instrument is useless if it is not adjusted correctly so that it functions in an orderly manner, however, and similarly our bodies are of no use to our higher organism if they do not function properly. Our freedom can be handicapped and intentions impeded.

140

When we as spiritual scientists consider our organism, we can ask ourselves if we do not make our bodies unfit for the execution of the intentions, aspirations and impulses of our lives if we become bound by and dependent upon our bodies through an unsuitable diet. Is it not possible to mould the body in such fashion that it turns into a progressively more suitable instrument for the impulses of our spiritual life? Will we lose our freedom and become dependent upon our bodies if we ignore what is the right nourishment for us? What must we eat so that we are not merely the product of what we eat?

By asking such questions, we come to look at the problem of nutrition from another perspective. You all know, and I only need allude to this generally familiar fact, that speaking purely materialistically, people continuously use up the substances that their organisms store and they therefore must take care to replenish them with further nourishment. Men must concern themselves with replenishment. What, then, could be more obvious than to examine those substances that are necessary for the human organism, that is, to find out what substances build up the animalistic organism, and then simply see to it that the organism is given them. This approach, however, remains an extremely materialistic one. We must rather ask ourselves what the essential task of a man's food is and in what way it is actually utilised in his organism.

I must stress that what I say about man is applicable only to him, since spiritual science does not consider man to be so closely connected with the animals as does natural science. Otherwise, one could simply state that the human organism is composed of proteins, fats, carbohydrates and mineral substances, and consequently search for the best method to satisfy man's nutritional needs of them. But spiritual science holds to the principle that every material occurrence, everything that takes place in the physical sense world, is only the external aspect of spiritual processes. Indeed, even the nutritional processes cannot be purely physical, but as material processes they are really the external aspects and expressions of spiritual processes. Similarly, man is a unity even though the composition of his physical body appears to be a conglomeration of chemical events.

Our attention has frequently been focused on how the ascent from the purely physical to the spiritual realm can be made. We have often heard that the physical body is sustained by the etheric body. This is the architect of the physical body, which must not be viewed as if only chemical processes took place in it. We will be wrong if, by observing only the chemical processes, we simply ask in a materialistic fashion what happens to the chemical substances. Beyond the etheric body, we must remember, is the astral body. Through it are expressed the instinctive feelings and in certain respects the various aspects of the soul. When we behold man from the standpoint of spiritual science, we find that his etheric body as well as his physical body are interpenetrated by his astral body. We must not see only one side but also perceive the astral body beyond the physical. Added to these is the ego, the fourth member of the human being. We have the total man before us only when we see in him this fourfold being. Only with the total fourfold man before us can we do justice to the scope of the problem of nutrition. Only then can answers be given to the question of how these four members of man's organism react to the influences of various diets.

Now, you all know that men eat food derived from the vegetable, animal and mineral kingdoms, and with it they sustain their bodies. Let me emphasise again for the sake of those who are more narrowly inclined toward the care of the inner life that I am not speaking to mystics nor to anthroposophists who are striving to develop themselves spiritually in particular, but to all men. Men take their sustenance from the animal, vegetable and mineral kingdoms. We must realise that plants represent the direct antithesis of men, and the animals represent the mean between the

142

two. The external physical expression of this contrast is to be found in the breathing process. It is a familiar fact that men inhale oxygen, assimilate it and subsequently combine it with carbon that is finally exhaled as carbon dioxide, while in plants, which absorb carbon to sustain themselves, the reverse is true. In a sense, plants also breathe but their breathing process has a completely different significance for them. Hence, we can say that in a spiritual respect plant and man stand opposite each other.

We can become even more aware of this relationship by bearing in mind the influence of light on plants. The effect of deprivation of light on plant life is well known. The same light that maintains life in plants makes it possible for us to perceive the light-filled world of our surroundings. Light is also the element that maintains life in plants. This is physical light but it is also something more. Just as there is a spiritual counterpart to everything physical, so there is spiritual light in the physical light that rays down on us. Each time a man rejoices over the brilliance of physical light he can say to himself, 'Just as when I see another person and it dawns on me that in this man there lives a spiritual counterpart, so also I can imagine that in light there lives a spiritual counterpart.' Indeed, the spiritual light that permeates the physical sunlight is of the same kind and being as the invisible light that dwells within the human astral body. A portion of the spiritual light that permeates the cosmic realm lives within the astral body. It is, however, physically invisible and in this it can be seen that it is the opposite or complement of physical light.

The invisible light lives within us and fulfills a definite task. We might say that since they are opposites, it is to physical light what negative magnetism is to positive magnetism. We perceive it in its external expression when we realise the relationships existing between physical body, etheric body and astral body, which, in turn, is permeated by the ego. It has often been explained that throughout life the etheric body fights against the deterioration of the physical body. Men as well as animals also possess an astral body and hence the inner light. Now, the function of this inner light is the opposite of that of external light. When external light shines on a plant, the plant builds up its living organism by producing proteins, carbohydrates, etc. Conversely, the task of inner light is to break down, and this process of disintegration is part of the activity of the astral body. There is indeed a continuous dissolution and destruction of the proteins and other substances that we consume so that these substances are utilised, in a sense, to direct counter-effects against what external light has built up. Without this activity of inner dissolution a man could not be an ego being, and it is only by virtue of his ego nature that he can have inner experiences. So, while the etheric body is concerned with the preservation of the physical body, the astral body takes care that the food a man consumes is constantly built up and again destroyed.

Without this process of disintegration within the physical body, the astral body, in which the ego is incorporated, could not live a full life within the material world. As we have seen, there is an alternating process obtaining between men and plants, that is, exhalation of carbon dioxide in men and absorption of carbon dioxide by plants; exhalation of oxygen by plants and inhalation of oxygen by men. These processes reach such extremes only between men and plants. Animals do not have individual egos as is the case with men, but they have collective group egos. Thus, the animals of a species have one common group ego that governs them from without. The significant difference between men and animals is found in the fact that the disintegration processes within animals are directed by an entity external to them, whereas the same processes in man are conducted by their individual inner egos. Moreover, a man's individual ego can gradually become master over what takes place within him.

Let us consider how the ego can gradually take a central

144

position within the bodily functions. Let us examine what the astral body does when it dissolves the substances assimilated by men. In regard to nourishment an entirely different viewpoint must be stressed. The body permeated by the ego performs an action in disintegrating substances, and through this action something is created inwardly. The inner activity of consciousness particularly comes about through the astral body's process of dissolution. Actions, activities are called forth by the process of destruction. First, inner warmth is produced and second, something that is less noticeable than inner body heat — the physical expression of inner light. Just as the internal warmth that permeates the blood is the result of the dissolution of proteins, so the activity of the nervous system is the expression of this inner light. In regard to its inner activity the nervous system is also a result of the disintegration process — not the nerves themselves but the activity of the nerves, the actions within the nerves, that which makes possible imagination and calls forth thinking. It is this activity that can be called the physical expression of the invisible light and that is brought about through the degeneration and dissolution of substances.

Basically, as has been said, inner body heat is generated by the disintegration of protein. Inner light is produced within the organism as a result of protein. Inner light is produced within the organism as a result of processes involving fats, carbohydrates, starches and glucose that are also utilised in the production of warmth and inner movement. In all this is contained the expression of the activity originating from the astral body. Men do not nourish themselves properly simply by ingesting the correct quantity of food, but rather when these inner processes can be carried out in the right way. The inner life is founded on them. Men are beings continually occupied inwardly with movement and liveliness and their inner life consists of these. If this inner life is not produced in the right way, it cannot react properly and a man then becomes ill.

The right kind of inner flexibility offers the foundation for the right solution of the nutritional problem. This statement points to the fact that all internal processes that men must execute must be carried on in the opposite direction from the processes of plants. A man must begin his processes where the plant processes leave off. A specific example will clarify what this means. When a man eats vegetarian food, it demands a great deal of his organism. Plant food does not contain much fat. The human organism, which is able to produce fats, is thus required to produce fat from something that in itself contains no fat. In other words, when a man eats vegetarian food, he must produce an activity within himself and make an inner effort to bring about the production of fats. He is spared this task when he eats readymade animal fats. The materialists would probably say that it is advantageous for a man to store up as much fat as possible without having to make too much of an effort. Yet, speaking from the spiritual viewpoint, the unfolding of this inner activity signifies the unfolding of the actual inner life. When a man is forced to produce the forces that make it possible for him to produce fat on his own, then, through his inner flexibility, the ego and the astral body become master of the physical and etheric bodies. When a man eats fat, he resultingly is spared the task of producing fat himself. Yet, if he takes the opportunity to unfold his own inner activity through producing his own fat, he is made free and thus becomes lord over his body. Otherwise, as a spiritual being he remains a mere spectator. Everything that takes place in him in such wise that he remains a passive spectator becomes a heavy weight in him and hinders his urge to let the astral body come to full life. Thus, the astral body's inner flexibility comes up against an internal obstacle if it is denied the opportunity to produce its own fat.

The essential question now to be asked is what internal activities are aroused by what substances. Here we shall try to throw light on the relationships of vegetable and meat substances in human diets, and thereby to gain some idea of the manner in which animal and vegetable foods react in the human organism.

For a man to eat animal protein is not the same as for him to eat plant protein. Up to a certain point the inner processes of the animal are quite similar to those of the human organism, since the animal also possesses an astral body. Even though the animal astral body causes the dissolution of the synthesised substances of its physical body the human organism carries the processes a bit beyond the limits reached by that of the animals.

In reflecting upon the animals around us and by looking spiritually into their ways and characteristics, we shall, by comparing men with the multitudes of animals, find distributed among the animals the various and manifold characteristics of men. In spite of the fact that one can point out great human differences between the various peoples, one must still conclude that each individual man represents a species. Men appear to be the spiritual con-solidation of all that can be observed distributed in the various animal forms. If one were to picture all the individual characteristics of the various animal species as being mutually complementary, one would arrive at the essence of what is contained in appropriate moderation in each individual man. Each individual animal one-sidedly contains within itself something of the forces that are harmonised within men, and its whole organism is constructed accordingly. Everything down to the most minute structure of substances is so organised in the animal kingdom that it is like a tableau of human characteristics spread out before one.

If a man is to find the physical expression of the charac-teristics of his astral body, he must strive to utilise all its forces. He must become master of his own inner processes and activate his astral body in such wise that the plant processes will be continued inwardly. In the food we consume from the animal kingdom, we not only take into ourselves the physical meat and fat of the animal but also the product of its astral body contained in these substances. When, through a vegetarian diet, we enlist the virginal forces of our astral body, we call forth our whole inner activity. In a meat diet part of this inner activity is forestalled.

We can now proceed to consider the relationships of these two types of diet from a purely spiritual basis.

If a man desires to gain an increasing mastery over the inner processes of his body, it is important that he become correspondingly active in the external world. It is important for him to unfold certain external qualities such as stamina, courage and even aggressiveness. To be able to do so, however, it is possible that a man may not yet find himself strong enough to entrust everything to his astral body and may have to fall back upon the support of a meat diet.

It can be said that man owes everything that liberates him internally to the substances derived from plants. Faculties, however, which enable him to be actively engaged in earthly life, need not necessarily grow out of the virginal nature of his astral body. These qualities can also be derived from a meat diet. This fact that men are to become progressively freer while at the same time needing qualities that they can acquire with the help of impulses found spread out in the animal kingdom, has induced them to resort to nourishment in animal food. If the eating habits of the people of those militant nations that have striven to develop qualities enabling them to unfold their physical forces are investigated, it will generally be found that they eat meat. Naturally, there are exceptions. On the other hand, a preference for an exclusively vegetarian diet will be found to prevail among people who have developed an introverted and contemplative existence. These two aspects of the problem should be kept in mind. A person, of course, can adopt either diet as a panacea if he wishes to propagandise rather than to act out of knowledge. Nevertheless, it is not without reason that a mixed diet has become acceptable to many people. To

148

some extent it had to happen. We must admit, however, that even though a vegetarian diet might indeed be the correct one for some people purely for reasons of health, the health of others might be ruined by it.

I am speaking here of human nature in general, of course, but men must be considered as individuals if they are to find the right path to satisfy their needs with a vegetable or meat diet. Today, an extreme diet of meat naturally brings its corresponding results. If by eating meat a person is relieved of too large a portion of his inner activities, then activities will develop inwardly that would otherwise be expressed externally. His soul will become more externally oriented, more susceptible to, and bound up with, the external world. When a person takes his nourishment from the realm of plants, however, he becomes more independent and more inclined to develop inwardly. He will become master over his whole being. The more he is inclined to vegetarianism, the more he accepts a vegetarian diet, the more he will be able also to let his inner forces predominate. Thus, the more apt he will be to develop a sense for wider horizons and he will no longer restrict himself to a narrow life. The person who is fundamentally a meat eater, however, limits himself to more narrow vistas and directs himself more rigidly toward one-sidedness.

Naturally, it is the task of men today to concern themselves with both aspects so as not to become impractical. A man also can be so completely unprejudiced as to have no judgment at all. Still, it is a fact that everything that limits men and leads them to specialisation is derived from a diet of meat. A man owes to a vegetarian diet the impulses that lift him above the narrow circles of existence. An extreme diet of meat is definitely connected with a man's increasing dogmatism and his inability to see beyond the confines into which he was born. In contrast, if men would show more interest in the food coming from the realm of plants, they would discover that they are able more easily

149

to lift themselves out of their narrow circles. The person who abandons the task of fat formation by eating meat will notice that the activity thus forestalled erects a sort of wall around his astral body. Even if one is not clairvoyant but judges these matters only with common sense, he can tell from the look in a person's eyes whether or not he produces his own fat. It can be seen in the eyes of a person whether or not his astral body is obliged to call forth the forces necessary to produce its own fat.

Now it can be seen how two opposing conditions of character are created when a person takes his nourishment from either the plants or animals. We find that we indeed penetrate into the world through our organism and must again rise above it by means of the right kind of food. A time will come when a vegetarian diet will be valued much more highly than is the case today. Then thinking will be so flexible that men will be willing to investigate such matters knowing that what they believe today to be foolishness could, viewed from another standpoint, also have its merits. They will realise then that their whole physical and spiritual horizon can be widened through a vegetarian diet, thus counteracting the rigour of specialisation within them. Particularly in certain areas of science would perspectives be widened if vegetarian diets should become prevalent.

Let me mention a few more examples to demonstrate that men are indeed what they eat and drink.

Consider, for example, alcohol, which is obtained from plants. It would take too long to explain the spiritual-scientific reason showing that alcohol produces physically and in an external way out of the plant, just what a man should develop physically within himself through his ego being centred within him. It is a fact inwardly perceived through spiritual science that when a person drinks alcohol, it takes over the specific activity that otherwise belongs wholly to the person's ego. A person who drinks much alcohol needs less food and his body will require less nourishment than is

150

normally required in the process of combustion. It calls forth forces that otherwise would be called forth by the ego's inner penetration. Thus, a person can externalise the activity of his ego by infusing his body with alcohol. Consequently, alcohol imitates and copies the activity of the ego, and you can understand why it is that people turn to it. To the extent, however, that a man replaces his inner self with such a substitute, to that extent does he become its slave. If otherwise qualified, a man will be better able to unfold the best forces of his ego when he abstains from alcohol altogether. By drinking alcohol an inner hindrance is created behind which something takes place that actually should and would be accomplished through the activity of the ego itself if the hindrance had not been produced.

Some foods have a specific effect of their own on the organism. Coffee is an example. The effect of coffee becomes manifest through its influence on the astral body. Through caffeine and the after-effects of coffee, our nervous systems automatically perform functions that we otherwise would have to produce through inner strength. It should not be claimed, however, that it is beneficial under all circumstances for a man always to act independently out of his astral body. Men are beings who are not dependent on themselves alone. Rather are they placed within the whole of life.

Coffee is also a product of the plant kingdom that externally has raised the specific plant process up a stage. Consequently, coffee can take over a certain task of man. Trained insight perceives that everything in the activity of our nerves that has to do with logical consistency and drawing conclusions is strengthened by coffee. Thus, we can let coffee take over in making logical connections and in sticking to one thought, but this, of course, is in exchange for a weakening of our specific inner forces. What I mean can be seen in the tendency of gossips at a coffee table to cling to a subject until it is completely exhausted. This is not only a joke. It also demonstrates the effects of coffee.

151

Tea works in a totally different and opposite way. When large quantities are drunk, thoughts become scattered and light. It might be said that the chief effect of tea is to let witty and brilliant thoughts, thoughts that have a certain individual lightness, flash forth. So we can say, coffee helps those, such as literary people, who need to connect thoughts in skilled and refined ways. This is the positive aspect of the matter. The negative aspect can be observed in coffee table gossip. Tea, which tears thoughts asunder, is the opposite. This is why tea is not without justification a popular drink of diplomats.

It might be of interest to cite as a last example a food that plays an important part in life, that is, milk. Milk is completely different from meat in that it expresses in the weakest possible form the animalistic process brought forth by the astral body of the animal. Milk is only partly an animal product and the animal or human astral forces do not participate in its production. For this reason milk is one of the most perfect foods. It is suitable for people who want to abstain completely from meat but who do not yet possess sufficient strength to work entirely out of the inner forces of the astral body. Even from a purely external standpoint it can be seen that milk contains everything a man requires for his organism. Although this applies only in a restricted sense, it has little to do with the individual characteristics of a man.

Weak as well as strong organisms can gain support from milk. If a person were to live exclusively on milk for a time, then not only would his regular forces be awakened but it would also go beyond this. He would receive from it an influx of forces giving him additional strength. A surplus of forces would be acquired that could be developed into healing forces. In order to possess a force, it must first be acquired, and in milk we see one means of developing certain forces in ourselves. Those who are moved by the earnestness of life to develop certain psychic healing forces, can train themselves to attain them. Naturally, we must remember that what is suitable for one, is not suitable for all. This is a matter for the individual. One person is able to do it, another not. A man can if he wishes build up his organism in a wise manner. He can contribute toward the unfolding of free, independent inner forces. So through spiritual science we come back to the saying of Feuerbach mentioned at the beginning, 'Man is what he eats!'

Man can nourish himself in such fashion that he undermines his invisible independence. In so doing he makes himself an expression of what he eats. Yet he ought to nourish himself in such a manner that he becomes less the slave of his nutritional habits. Here spiritual science can direct him.

The wrong food can easily transform us into what we eat, but by permeating ourselves with knowledge of the spiritual life, we can strive to become free and independent. Then the food we eat will not hinder us from achieving the full potential of what we, as men, ought to be.

24

INFLUENCE OF THE VARIOUS PARTS OF PLANTS
ON THE HUMAN ORGANISM

From: *The World of the Senses.*
Extract from: Lecture 6   Hanover, 1st January 1912

One will come to recognise that what rests in the seed is
connected in a different way with man than what is contained
in the root. What is contained in the root of a plant corresponds in a way to the human brain and to the nervous
system belonging to the brain. This goes so far in actual
fact that the eating of what is contained in plant roots
has a certain relationship with the processes which take
place in the brain and nervous system. So if a man wants
his brain and nervous system to be influenced physically
as physical instrument for the life of the spirit, he should
take in with his food the forces which are in the roots of
plants. Thus in a certain way, he lets what he receives in
his food think in him — do spiritual work in him — while
if he is less inclined to eat roots it will more be himself,
his spirituality, which uses his brain and nervous system.
You will see from this that a diet rich in roots gives man
a lack of independence in his soul/spiritual life, because
something objective and external works in him, his brain
and nervous system become independent of him. So when,
in a higher degree, *he* wants to be the one who works within
himself, then he must cut down on roots. My dear friends,
this is no recommendation for any particular diet, but
only information about facts of nature, and I warn you
expressly not to take these things as rules to follow. Not
everyone is so far advanced as to be able to dispense with
receiving the power of thought from something outside

himself. It may very easily happen that someone who is not yet ready to rely on his own soul life to provide him with the power of thinking and feeling, and yet avoids eating roots, will fall into a kind of sleepy condition because his soul and spirit are not yet strong enough to develop the forces out of his own inner being which normally are developed objectively and independently of his soul and spirit. This is how it is. All diets are completely individual and depend entirely on the manner and condition of development of the person in question.

What lives in the leaves of plants has a rather similar connection with the lungs and all that belongs to that system. Here we can find an indication of how a balance can be created, for example, in a person whose breathing system, owing to inherited tendencies or some other condition, is too strong. He would be well advised not to eat too much of what comes from the leaves of plants. A person whose breathing system requires strengthening is well advised to eat as much leaf food as possible. These things have their close connection with the healing forces which are in the world in the kingdoms of nature, for those parts of individual plants which have a definite relationship to such organs contain forces of healing for these regions of the human organism. Thus roots contain great forces of healing for the nervous system, and leaves for the lung system.

Flowers of plants contain many healing forces for the kidney system, for instance, and seeds contain in a certain way healing forces for the heart, but only for a condition when the heart resists the circulation of the blood too strongly. If the heart gives in too easily to the circulation, then it is rather to the forces that are in fruits i.e. in the ripened seed, that we must turn. These are some of the indications that follow when we take into consideration that the moment we pass from man to surrounding nature all that presents itself to our senses in the world of nature is actually only the surface.

Summary

Roots   : Brain
Leaves : Lungs
Flowers : Kidneys
Seeds   : Heart
Fruits : Blood system

25

MEAT. VEGETARIAN FOOD. ALCOHOL

From: *The Effects of Spiritual Development.*
Extract from: Lecture 1   The Hague, 20th March 1913

Since we are dealing here with the physical body, we must
first describe the nature of meat and vegetarian food and
food in general. All this should be an element in discussing
the influences of an anthroposophical way of life upon the
sheaths of man. This may be called the replenishing, the
regeneration of the physical body from outside through the
ingestion of outer substances. Man's relation to his food is
only rightly understood when we keep in view his relation
to the other kingdoms of nature, beginning with the plant
kingdom. The plant kingdom as a realm of life brings the
inorganic substances, the lifeless substances, up to a certain
stage of organisation. For the living plant to arise, it is
necessary that the lifeless substances be transformed to a
certain stage of organisation as in a living laboratory. In the
plant we have a living being which develops the lifeless
products of nature to a certain stage of organisation. Physical
man is able to take up this process where the plant has left
off and to carry it on from there so that the higher organisation — man — arises. There is perfect continuity when man
picks an apple or a leaf and eats it. It is the most perfect
continuity. If all things were so designed that what is most
natural could be done, one could say that the most natural
thing would be for man to continue the process of organisation where the plant has left off i.e. to take the parts of the
plant as he finds them in nature and develop and organise
them further within himself. That would be a straight line
of organising, which would not be interrupted anywhere in

any way, from the lifeless substance up to the point of the organisation of the plant, and from here to the human organism.

Let us now take the most straightforward case. Man eats the animal. The animal is a living being which takes the process of organisation further than the plant does, to a certain point above the plant organisation. We can say of the animal that it continues the process of organisation begun by the plant. Let us assume that man eats the animal. What now happens is that it is no longer necessary for man to use the inner forces he would have needed had he eaten a plant. Had he been obliged to organise the foodstuff from where the plant left off, he would have had to use a certain sum of forces. These now remain unused when he eats the animal, for it has already carried the plant organisation to a certain higher point. This is where man has now to begin. So we can say that if man does not continue the process of organising from where he could begin, he leaves forces unused and continues the organising from a later stage. He lets the animal do part of the work he would have had to do if he had eaten the plant. Now the well-being of an organism does not consist in doing as little as possible, but in activating all its forces. If a man eats plants he uses forces which engender organic activities; if he eats meat he does with these forces what a man would do if he said: I will do without my left arm, I will tie it up so that it cannot be used. Thus he fetters his inner forces when he eats meat, forces which he would call upon if he ate plants. So he condemns a certain sum of forces within him to inactivity. Everything that is condemned to inactivity in the human organism causes the respective system — which ought to be active — to lie fallow and to become disabled and hardened. So when a man eats meat he kills a part of his organism, or at least disables it. The part of his organism which becomes hardened he carries through life like a foreign body. In normal life he does not feel this foreign body. But if the

158

organism becomes inwardly flexible and mobile and his various systems of organs become independent of one another, as is brought about when we live with anthroposophy, then the physical body, which as we said already feels uncomfortable, begins to feel even more uncomfortable because it contains a foreign body. Now I do not proselytise, I merely want to state the truth. We shall get to know still other effects of meat diet; we shall be obliged to discuss this subject in some detail. This is why progress in inner anthroposophical life gradually produces a sort of revulsion against meat. It is not as though one has to forbid meat to anthroposophists, but the healthily progressing instinct gradually turns against meat and no longer likes it. And this is much better than becoming a vegetarian out of some abstract principle. The best is when spiritual science causes man to develop a kind of aversion for meat. With regard to higher development there is no virtue in breaking oneself of the habit of eating meat in any other way. So one can say that meat diet becomes a burden to the physical body of man and this burden is felt. This is the occult fact seen from one aspect.

We will characterise this from yet another side. I would like to mention alcohol as another example. Man's relationship to alcohol will also change when he takes up anthroposophy earnestly and it quickens his inner life. Alcohol is something quite special in the realms of nature. It does not only produce a burden for the human organism but becomes a veritable opposing power. The plant, as we have seen, carries its organisation up to a certain point, but here the grape vine is an exception. It goes a step further. What all the other plants save for the future germinating seed — the driving force that is reserved for the future sprouting and which does not spread through the rest of the plant — in the vine pours in a way into the fruit — the grape — so that through the fermentation, through the transformation of that which poured into the grape, and there in the grape itself reaches the highest tension, something is produced which has a power in the plant which can only be likened occultly to the power which the human ego has over the blood. Thus what arises in the making of wine and the production of alcohol takes place in another kingdom, but man should create it himself when he, from his ego, acts on the blood.

We know that there is an intimate connection between the ego and the blood. This can be seen outwardly when the ego feels shame and the person blushes, while with fear he grows pale. The action of the ego on the blood — which is always taking place — is occultly very similar to what takes place when the plant process is reversed, which happens when the grape or any vegetable matter is transformed into alcohol. Normally the ego must induce in the blood a process, very similar — occultly not chemically — to the production of alcohol which is the reversal of the normal plant process. Consequently alcohol introduces into the organism something which, from another direction, acts like the ego upon the blood. With alcohol we take into ourselves an anti-ego, an ego which directly opposes the deeds of our own spiritual ego. From the opposite side alcohol acts upon the blood in the same way as the ego acts upon the blood. Thus an inner war breaks out which renders the ego powerless. This is the occult fact. Those who drink no alcohol make sure that they are free to let their ego act on the blood. He who drinks alcohol behaves like someone who wishes to knock down a wall but puts someone on the other side to counter his blows. In the same way the consumption of alcohol eliminates the action of the ego on the blood. Hence a person who makes anthroposophy the central element of his life feels the action of alcohol in the blood as a direct battle against his ego, and it is therefore quite natural that a true spiritual development only comes easily if one does not impose this counterforce.

26

MILK, PLANT FOODS, MEAT, PROTEIN, FATS, SUGAR, COFFEE, TEA, CHOCOLATE

From: *The Effects of Spiritual Development.*
Extract from: Lecture 2   The Hague, 21st March 1913

We know from experience that when we eat meat our physical sheath bears a heavier burden than when we eat vegetarian food. Now when meat is consumed, this meat appears as a foreign body in the human organism, like a lead weight in the body. In esoteric development one feels the earthly weight of meat more than one normally does and one experiences particularly that meat diet inflames the instinctive nature of the will. This rather unconscious will which appears as emotions and passions is inflamed by meat eating. Therefore the observation that warlike peoples are more inclined to eat meat than peaceful ones, is quite correct. But this should not lead to the belief that vegetarian food drives out courage and vigour. Indeed we shall see that what a person loses in the way of instincts and aggressive passions when he forgoes meat — this will be dealt with in connection with the astral body — will be compensated from within, from the soul. All these things are connected with the whole relationship of man to the cosmos and the other kingdoms of nature, and one gradually receives — even if not through higher clairvoyance — a kind of confirmation of what the occultist has to say concerning the relationship of human life to the cosmos. We receive a kind of proof if, by experiencing the processes of the physical body which have become more active and mobile, we feel, so to speak, in our own body the nature and characteristics of earthly substances used as food.
It is interesting to compare three kinds of food with

regard to their cosmic significance: (1) milk and milk products, (2) the plant world and all that is made from it, (3) meat. We can compare milk, plants and animals as foods when, through esoteric development, we have become more sensitive to the effects of these foods. It will then be easier to evaluate what is confirmed by a rational observation of the outer world. If, as an occultist, you would explore the universe you would find the substance milk only on the earth but on no other planet of our solar system. What is produced in a similar way by organisms on other planets in our solar system would be found to be completely different from our earthly milk. Milk is specifically earthly and if one would specify what milk is, we should have to say that the organisms of each planetary system have their own particular milk.

If we investigate the plant nature on our earth and compare it occultly with the plant nature of other planets — or with what can be compared with it — we must say that the form of the plant being on earth is different from the plant being on other planets of our solar system; but the essential nature of the plant on earth is not purely terrestrial but something that belongs to the whole solar system, i.e. the plant being of our earth is related to the plant being of the other planets of our solar system. Thus in our plants we have something extending into our system which can also be found on other planets.

As for the animal kingdom, it follows from what has been said about milk, and it can easily be proved by the occultist, that the animal kingdom of our earth is radically different from any corresponding kingdom on other planets.

Now let us consider how we experience milk as a food. To occult vision milk is, for the human body, (we will limit ourselves to man) that element which binds him to the earth, to our planet. It connects him with the human race on the earth, as a member of the common species of mankind. Mankind, as regards the physical system of sheaths, forms one whole; partly owing to the production of nourishment by living beings for living beings of the same species. What is given to the human organism in milk prepares him to be a human creature of the earth, unites him with the conditions of the earth, but does not really fetter him to the earth. It makes him a citizen of the earth, but does not hinder him from being a citizen of the whole solar system.

It is different with meat. Meat is taken from that kingdom which is specifically earthly, it is not like milk taken from the actual life-process of the human or animal being, but it is taken from that part of the animal substance which is prepared ready for the animal. This meat really fetters man to the earth. It makes him into a creature of the earth, so that we must say that to the extent that man permeates his organism with the effects of meat in his food, he deprives himself of the forces which would enable him to free himself from the earth. Through meat diet he binds himself very strongly to the planet earth. Whilst milk enables him to belong to the earth as a transitory stage in his development, meat condemns him – unless he is raised up by something else – to make his sojourn on earth like a permanent one to which he adapts himself completely. If I decide to take milk it means: 'I will sojourn on the earth so that I may fulfil my mission there but I will not exist exclusively for the earth.' The will to eat meat means: 'I like the earthly existence so well that I renounce all heaven and prefer to be wholly absorbed in the conditions of earthly existence.'

Vegetarian diet stimulates those forces in the organism which bring man into a kind of cosmic connection with the whole of the planetary system. What man has to accomplish when he further transforms vegetarian food in his organism stimulates forces which are contained in the whole solar system, so that man in his physical sheath participates in the forces of the whole solar system; he does not become alien to them, he does not tear himself away from them. This is something which the soul in the course of its

163

anthroposophical or esoteric development can experience, for it takes in with the plant something not pertaining to the heaviness of the earth, but to the sun, i.e. the central body of the entire planetary system. The lightness of the organism which results from a vegetarian diet lifts one out of the heaviness of the earth, and gradually one develops a capacity of experience that can develop by degrees into something like a perception of taste in the human organism. It feels — this organism — as though it shared with the plants the very sunlight which accomplishes so much in them.

From what has been said you will gather that in occult, esoteric development it is of tremendous importance not to fetter oneself, as it were, to the earth, not to encumber oneself with the heaviness of the earth through the consumption of meat if it can be dispensed with in view of individual and hereditary circumstances. The ultimate decision must depend upon the personal circumstances of the individual. It will facilitate the whole development of man's life if he can refrain from eating meat. On the other hand certain difficulties will arise if a person becomes a fanatical vegetarian in the sense of rejecting milk and all milk products. In the development of the soul towards the spiritual this brings certain dangers, simply because, in avoiding milk and all milk products, a person may easily develop a love solely for that which detaches him from the earth and he may thus lose the threads which connect him with all human activities on the earth. Therefore the striving anthroposophist should be warned not to allow himself to become a fanatical spiritual dreamer by creating the difficulty in his physical sheath which will separate it from all relationship to what is earthly and human. In order that we may not become too eccentric when striving for soul development, in order that we may not become estranged from human feeling and human doings, it is well for us as pilgrims on earth to take on 'ballast' through consumption of milk and milk products. And it may even be a really systematic training for a person

164

who is not in a position, so to speak, to live perpetually in the spiritual world and thereby become a stranger on earth, but who besides this has to fulfill his duties on earth; it can be a systematic training not to be a strict vegetarian but to take milk and milk products as well. He will thereby relate his organism, his physical sheath, to the earth and to humanity, but not fetter it to the earth and weigh it down as would be the case with eating meat.

Thus it is interesting in every way to see how these things are connected with cosmic secrets, and how through the knowledge of these cosmic secrets we can follow the actual effect of food substances in the human organism.

As people who are interested in occult truths you must let it sink into you more and more that what appears on our earth — and our physical body belongs to our earthly existence — does not depend only on earthly conditions and forces but also on forces and conditions of extra-terrestrial intelligences, cosmic intelligences. This comes about in various ways. Thus, for example, if we consider the albumen as contained in the hen's egg, we must clearly understand that such animal protein is not merely what the chemist finds in his analysis, but that, in its structure, it is the result of cosmic forces. When we speak of protein it is in its structure a product of cosmic forces which acted first on the earth itself and also on the moon which accompanies the earth. Thus the cosmic influence upon animal protein is an indirect one. The cosmic forces do not work directly upon albumen, but indirectly. They first act upon the earth, and the earth with its forces, derived from the cosmos, acts on the composition of the animal protein. The moon at best, takes a share in it but only to the extent that it rays back to the animal protein the forces which it derives from the cosmos. In the smallest cell of animal substance and therefore also in protein, occult vision can see that not only the physical and chemical forces belonging to the earth are present in it, but that the smallest cell of an egg is built up of the forces which the earth first obtains from the cosmos. Thus the substance we call protein is indirectly connected with the cosmos, but this animal protein as it exists on earth would never come into being if the earth were not there. It could not arise directly out of the cosmos, it is absolutely a product of what the earth has first to receive from the cosmos.

It is different with what we know as fats from living creatures which are part of the diet of meat eaters. We will speak of these animal fats. What we call fat, irrespective of whether we eat it or produce it in our own organism, is built up according to entirely different cosmic laws from protein. While the cosmic forces producing protein proceed from the hierarchy of the Spirits of Form, those concerned with building up fats are mainly the Spirits of Movement. You see it is important to mention such things because they give us the idea how complicated in reality is something which external science imagines to be so simple. No living being could have within it protein as well as fats if the Spirits of Form and Spirits of Movement did not work together from the cosmos — even though indirectly.

Thus we can trace the spiritual activities proceeding from the beings of the various hierarchies into the very substances of which our physical sheath is composed. When the soul has undergone anthroposophical development, the experiences one has of the protein and of the fat in one's physical body become more differentiated, more sensitive. It is a twofold experience. That which in the normal life of man is merged into a single experience — the action of the fats and proteins — he experiences intermingled. As the whole physical organism becomes more responsive, the developing soul learns to distinguish two different sensations in the body, one which permeates us inwardly so that we feel: 'this forms me into a whole and gives me stature.' With this we feel the protein in us. When we feel: 'This makes us indifferent to our inner self-containment, this lifts us in a

166

sense out of our form, it makes us more phlegmatic with respect to our inner feelings when there is a certain phlegma with regard to our experiences — the experiences become differentiated very much with anthroposophical development — then the origin of this feeling is the inner experience of the fat in the physical body. Thus our inner experience of the physical body becomes more complex.

We perceive this particularly in experiencing starch or sugar. Sugar is particularly characteristic. In the appreciation of taste, sugar is very different from other substances. This difference can easily be seen in ordinary life, not only in children, but sometimes in older people in their liking for sugar, but usually this is restricted to the taste. When the soul undergoes development it experiences the substance of sugar which it takes in or has within itself as something that gives it inner stability, inner support, and permeates it as it were with a kind of natural egohood. In this respect one can extol the virtues of sugar. People who are developing spiritually quite often find they need sugar because their soul development should make them progressively more selfless. Through a sound anthroposophical development the soul becomes inevitably more selfless. Now in order that a man — by virtue of his physical body having a mission on earth — may not lose the connection of his ego-organism with the earth, it is good to create a counterpoise in the physical body where egoity is of the same significance as it is in the realm of morality. The consumption of sugar creates, as it were, a kind of innocent egoity which may form a counterpoise to the necessary selflessness in the moral and spiritual sphere. Otherwise there might all too easily be the temptation, not only to become selfless but also to become dreamy and live in a world of unreality and lose the ability to maintain a capacity for sound judgement on earthly matters. The addition of a certain quantity of sugar to the food enables us to remain with both feet on the earth and cultivate a healthy outlook on earthly affairs in spite of rising to the spiritual worlds.

167

As you see, these things are complicated. But things become complicated when one begins to penetrate the real secrets of life. Thus, as one's soul advances anthroposophically, one sometimes feels that in order not to fall prey to a false selflessness, to a loss of one's personality, one feels at times that one needs sugar. One experiences the eating of sugar so that one says: 'Now I am adding to myself something that, without lowering myself morally, gives me, as if involuntarily, as though by a higher instinct, a certain stability, a certain egoity. On the whole one can say that the consumption of sugar enhances the personality in a physical way. We can be so certain of this that we may even say that it is easier for those who take sugar to express their personality in their physical body than for those who do not take sugar; but it stands to reason that this must be kept within healthy limits. These things can make understandable what we can actually observe. In countries where, statistically, little sugar is eaten, the people have a less defined personality than in countries where more sugar is eaten. If you go to countries where the people show more individuality, where people appear more as individuals and feel this inwardly, and then move on to countries where the people show a more general type, show less personality as external physical beings, you will find that in the former countries sugar consumption is high and in the latter very little sugar is eaten.

If we wish to have still more obvious examples of the effects of foods, let us consider certain stimulants. One is vividly aware of these in ordinary life, especially of coffee and tea. The effect on a normal person is greatly heightened in the case of a person undergoing anthroposophical development. As I have said already, this is not a campaign for or against coffee, but simply a statement of things as they are, and I beg you to take it in this sense. Even in normal life coffee and tea act as stimulants but the stimulating effects on the organism are felt more vividly by the soul undergoing spiritual development. The action of coffee causes the human organism to lift its etheric body in a certain way out of the physical body, but in such a manner that the physical body is felt as a solid foundation for the etheric body. That is the specific action of coffee. When coffee is taken the physical body and etheric body become differentiated but in such a way that one feels the characteristics of form of the physical body radiating into the etheric body. The physical body is felt as a kind of solid foundation for what is experienced through the etheric body. This must not be taken as a defence of coffee-drinking, for it rests upon a physical basis, and man would become a completely dependent being if he wanted to prepare himself spiritually by the use of these stimulants; we merely want to characterise the influence of these stimulants. But because logical, consecutive thinking depends very much upon the structure and form of the physical body, the peculiar action of coffee gives a sharper emphasis to the physical structure and promotes logical consistency physically. By drinking coffee, logical consistency, consecutive thinking derived from facts, is promoted by physical means, and it can be said that even though for health reasons there may be doubts about drinking much coffee, yet for those who wish to ascend to the higher regions of spiritual life, it is not amiss. It may be quite good occasionally to obtain logical consistency by means of coffee. One might say that it seems quite natural for a person whose profession is writing and who does not quite find the logical sequence from one sentence to the next and tries to suck it out of his pen, to make use of the stimulus of coffee. This seems comprehensible to one who knows how to observe the secret occult foundations of these things. As citizen of the earth we sometimes need this drink according to the individual circumstances and it must be emphasised that coffee, despite all its faults, can contribute to the increase of stability. Not that it should be recommended as a means of developing stability, but it must be said that it has the power of so doing and that if, for example, someone undergoing anthroposophical development has the tendency of letting his thoughts stray in the wrong direction, we need not take it amiss if he stabilises himself with coffee.

It is different with tea. The action of tea is comparable. The physical and etheric nature become differentiated, but in a certain way the structure of the physical body is not engaged. The etheric body comes into its own — its fluctuating nature. As a result the thoughts are made to flit about and are less able to keep to facts. Imagination is stimulated by tea but sometimes not in a very nice way and what is not stimulated is adherence to the truth and to solid facts. It is therefore understandable that in social gatherings where flashes of wit and sparkling intellect are demanded, the stimulation is readily provided by tea. On the other hand when tea-drinking becomes an excessive habit it produces a certain indifference to the demands arising from the healthy structure of the physical body. So idle fantasy, an unconcerned nonchalance which likes to ignore the detailed demands of practical life, is encouraged by tea-drinking. And in the case of a person undergoing anthroposophical development tea is not recommended since it can lead more easily to charlatanism than coffee does. The latter makes for greater stability, the former for greater charlatanism, though the word is much too severe in this case. All these are things which one can experience thanks to the mobility which an anthroposophical training brings to the physical sheath of man.

I would simply like to add — and you can meditate further on these things or try to experience them personally — that if coffee-drinking promotes something like stability in the physical sheath and tea favours charlatanism, then chocolate promotes philistinism. Chocolate is the true beverage of the bourgeoisie. This can be experienced when the physical body becomes more mobile. Chocolate can therefore be recommended for bourgeois festivities and one can well understand that it is drunk in certain circles on festive occasions such as family festivals, birthdays, etc. When we bear in mind that these things are stimulants, their influence assumes a greater significnace, because what we normally experience with regard to foodstuffs influences our ordinary daily life in such a way that not only are we aware of the substances of which the body is made and which are constantly renewed, but we are also made aware, as was mentioned yesterday, of the separation, the inner dissociation of the organs, from each other. That is important and very significant.

27

AN ASPECT OF THE PROCESS OF DIGESTION

From: *The Driving Force of Spiritual Powers in World History.*

Extract from: Lecture 6   Dornach, 22nd March 1923

When we eat plants we absorb not only their chemical constituents, not only the actual substances of the plant, but also the etheric life forces; but we must, as I have said here before, destroy them completely during the process of nutrition. When feeding on a living substance it is necessary for man to kill it completely within himself. He must therefore extract the etheric from the plant substance.

In the lower man, in the metabolic system, the following remarkable process takes place. When we eat plants, that is to say, vegetable substance — the same also applies to cooked foodstuffs but is especially marked when we eat raw pears, apples or berries — we force out the etheric and absorb into our own ether body the dynamic structure which underlies the plant. The plant has a definite form. It is revealed to clairvoyant consciousness that the form we thus take into ourselves is not always identical with the form we see externally. It is something different. The form of the plant wells up within us and adapts itself to the organism in a remarkable way.

And now something very strange occurs. Just suppose — one must speak rather paradoxically here but it is exactly how things are — suppose you have eaten some cabbage. A definite shape lights up in the lower man and an activity takes place in the metabolic system, as a result of eating the cabbage. To the extent to which this activity is engendered in the lower man by eating cabbage, the actual negative of it appears in the upper man, the head man — I should like to say, an empty space which corresponds to it, a copy, a real negative. So if we have this form in the lower man, in the upper man there arises the negative — a hollow form. It is a fact that the cabbage produces in us a definite form, and its negative arises in our head.

And into this negative of the cabbage we now receive the outer world. It can pour its impressions into us because we carry this hollow space within us, as it were. (I am of course only speaking approximately.) All nutritive plants have this effect.

•

28

MILK AND HONEY

From: *Man as Symphony of the Creative Word.*
Extract from: Lecture 11   Dornach, 10th November 1923

You see, the head is enclosed on all sides. In this head are
the impulses used during childhood for the formation of the
body. In the rest of the body the bones are inside and the
formative forces outside. The formative forces of the head
must be stimulated from outside. When we bring milk into
the head these formative forces will be stimulated when we
are children. When we are no longer children these forces
are no longer there. So what should we do in order to
stimulate these formative forces from outside?

It would obviously be good if what the head does inside
itself, enclosed as it is within the skull, could be done from
outside in the same way. It would be good if one could do
from outside what the head does within itself. The forces
which are inside the head are suited to the consumption of
milk. When the milk is there in its etheric transformation,
it provides a good basis for the development of the head
forces. We should therefore have something like milk which
however is not made within the human being but outside.

Well, there is something in nature which is a head without
a skull. The same forces work from without which work
inside the head where they need the milk and even create it
anew, because the child has to transform the milk into the
condition of warmth ether and then create it anew.

Now, the bee-hive is a head which is open on all sides.
What the bees do is actually the same in the outside world
as what the head does inside. However, it is not enclosed
but acts from outside. (We supply the hive only as a support.)

In the bee-hive we have, under external spiritual influences, the same thing as we have under spiritual influences inside the head. We have the honey in the bee-hive and if, as an older person, we take the honey and eat it, it gives us the formative forces from without with the same power and strength which milk gives to the head during childhood.

While we are children we promote the shaping forces from the head by drinking milk. If we need these forces in later life we have to eat honey and we do not have to eat it in enormous quantities — we depend on it only for its forces.

One can read from outer nature how to bring the necessary impulses into human life, if one understands this outer nature completely. And if one would want to imagine a land where there are beautiful children and beautiful old people, what kind of a land would this be? It would be 'a land flowing with milk and honey'. So you see, ancient instinctive vision was not wrong when it said of lands one longs for, that they flow with milk and honey.

29

THE WORK OF THE EGO-ORGANISATION

From: *World History in the Light of Anthroposophy.*
End of Lecture 7   Dornach, 30th December 1923

The ego-organisation stands in a special relationship with all that is mineral in man. Thus when you take in some mineral substance — for instance put some salt on your tongue — the ego-organisation will at once take hold of it. And even as the substance proceeds into the stomach the ego-organisation remains with it all the time. The salt goes still further, it undergoes various changes, passes through the intestines and goes on, but never will the ego-organisation leave your salt. They behave like two things which belong to one another — the ego-organisation and the salt that enters man.

It is quite different when you eat a fried egg or any other protein substance. The ego-organisation is only very little concerned when you have a bit of fried egg on your tongue. The astral body is also very little concerned with it as it slips down into the stomach. Then as it goes further on, first the etheric body and then the physical body act intensively upon it. Within your organism they break down the protein of the egg you have eaten. The egg is made completely mineral within you. It is broken down. All life is driven out of it. It is destroyed within you. At the walls of the intestines the protein that you have taken in ceases to be protein and becomes entirely mineral. Now it passes to the ego-organisation and from then onwards the mineralised protein is taken care of by the ego-organisation.

So we can say that the ego-organisation only concerns itself with what is mineral, but everything that is mineral becomes something different in the human organism from what it was outside. Nothing must remain as it was when it was outside the human organism. The ego-organisation must see to this thoroughly. Not only such substances as salt and the like are seized upon by the ego-organisation and changed into something different from what they were outside, but even the external warmth which surrounds one must never be allowed to penetrate the human being. You must never have your fingers filled with the warmth that is around you as external warmth. This warmth can but act as a stimulus, you yourself must create and produce the warmth that you have within you.... It is the nature of the ego-organisation that it takes up everything that is mineral and transforms it completely.

Not until we have died does the mineral again become the mineral of external nature. While we live on earth and carry mineral substances within our skin, our ego-organisation transforms them constantly. The plant substances which we eat are continually transformed by our astral organisation. Man's ego-organisation thoroughly metamorphoses all that is mineral, not only the solid, but also the fluid, the aeriform and the mineral in the form of heat.

One can of course say roughly speaking: Here is some water. I drink it. Now I have the water within me. But the moment my organism absorbs the water within me, my ego-organisation makes it into something different from what the water was outside. It only becomes the same again when I sweat it out or in some other way convert it into water. Within my skin water is not water but a living fluid.

177

30

THE EFFECT OF COOKING. THE TOMATO.

From: *Agriculture*.
Extracts from: Lecture 8.   Koberwitz, 16th June 1924

Fruiting processes which have not yet been carried to their final stage (nature does not carry everything to its final stage) can always be enhanced by processes which are somewhat akin to burning. Things like chopped roots (such as fodder beet and mangels or dried sugar beet pulp) will be improved if they are spread out in the sunlight. The inner tendency is thus led a little further towards the fruiting process. There is a wonderful instinct in these matters. Look at the world intelligently and you will ask: 'Why did it ever occur to man to cook his food?' It is a question, only one usually does not ask questions about what one is familiar with. Why did man come to cook his food? Because by and by he discovered that cooking, burning, heating, drying and steaming play a considerable part in leading plant substances towards the fruiting process. These processes will all encourage the flower and seed (and indirectly the other parts of the plant also, and particularly those that lie towards the upper regions) to develop more strongly the forces that have to be developed in the metabolic and limb system. Take just the flower or seed — the flower and seed work on the metabolic or digestive system, and they work there chiefly by their forces, not their substance.... So everything in the plant world which does not waste much time on leaf and foliage, but proliferates in flowers and fruit — that is what we ought to cook..

Man would do well to observe these things. If he did so we should have fewer of those movements which originate from people who are upon the downward slope, the inclined plane of laziness. They say to themselves no doubt: 'If I spend the whole day doing things, I can never become a true mystic. I can only become a true mystic if I am quiet and restful. I must not always be compelled — by my own needs or by the needs of those around me — to be up and doing. I must be able to say to my surrounding world: I have not the strength for all this work. Then I shall be able to become a true mystic. Therefore I will also endeavour to arrange my food so that I may become a proper mystic.' And from then on they will only eat raw food. They will have no more cooking. They will go in for raw food only.

These things are of course easily masked; they do not always emerge in this way. If someone who is well on the inclined plane to mysticism of this kind becomes an un- cooked food addict — and if from the outset he has a weak physical constitution — he will make good progress, he will become more and more indolent i.e. mystical.

.... However it can also be otherwise. The person may be physically strong and only afterwards become so 'cranky' as to want to become a mystic. He may have strong physical forces in him. Then the processes he has within him — and in addition the forces which the raw food calls forth in him — will develop strongly and it cannot do him much harm. For as he eats the raw food he will summon the forces which would otherwise remain latent and create rheumatism and arthritis. He will summon the forces and transform them and thus grow all the stronger.

Thus there are two sides to every question and we must realise how individual all these things are. We cannot give hard and fast rules. The advantage of the vegetarian mode of life is that it makes us stronger because we draw forth from the organism forces which would otherwise lie fallow. These are in fact the very forces that produce arthritis, rheumatism, diabetes and the like.

If one eats plant food only, these forces are used to raise

179

the plant and make it ready for the human being. If, on the other hand, we eat meat these forces are left latent in the organism. They remain unused and start using themselves up, depositing metabolic products in various parts of the organism. . . .

* * * * *

You know that in comparatively recent times the tomato has been introduced as a regular food. Many people like it. Now the tomato is a most important object of study. Much can be learned from the production and consumption of tomatoes. People who think about these things a little — and there are such people — find, and rightly so, that the consumption of tomatoes by man is of great significance. . . . It is in fact very significant that the tomato, when taken into the organism, separates itself from it, and creates its own organisation within the organism.

Two things follow from this. First, it confirms the statement of an American to the effect that tomatoes, under certain circumstances, have a most beneficial effect on a morbid tendency of the liver, because the liver is the organ that works with the greatest relative independence in the human body. So that, generally speaking, disorders of the liver could be counteracted by tomatoes.

In parenthesis, I may add that a person who has a carcinoma should at once be forbidden to eat tomatoes because carcinoma is itself something that has made itself independent within the human or animal organism. Now let us ask ourselves: Why is this? Why does the tomato work especially upon what is independent within the organism — upon what isolates itself from the organism as something special? This is connected with what the tomato wants and needs for its own growth.

The tomato is happiest if it receives manure as far as possible in its original form as excreted from the animal or otherwise fallen out of a life process — manure that has not had time to be worked on by nature — raw dung. If you have any kind of refuse, not yet on a proper compost heap, and you throw it together, as far as possible in its original state, not prepared, and you plant tomatoes in it, you will see that you get the finest tomatoes. Nay, more, if you use compost made of the tomato plant itself — stem, foliage and all — if you let the tomato grow on its own manure, it will develop splendidly.

The tomato does not want to go outside of itself; it does not want to leave the realm of its strong vitality. It wants to remain within it. It is the most uncompanionable plant in the vegetable kingdom. It does not want to get anything from outside. Above all, it rejects any manure that has already undergone a process of decomposition. It does not like it. From this stems its power to influence any independent organisation within the human or animal organism.

The potato in this respect is, to some extent, akin to the tomato. The potato, too, works in a highly independent way and it passes easily through the digestive process, penetrates into the brain and makes the brain independent — independent even of the influence of the other organs of the body. Indeed, the excessive use of potatoes is among the factors that have made men and animals materialistic since the introduction of the potato into Europe. We should only eat just enough potatoes to stimulate our brain and head-nature. The eating of potatoes, above all, should not be overdone.

31

HEALTHY INSTINCT FOR FOOD

Extract from: *The Education of the Child* (1907).

One thing that must emphatically be allowed for at this age (up to seven years) is that the physical body finds its own yardstick for what is good for it. This it does by the proper development of desire. Generally speaking we may say that the healthy physical body asks for what it needs. In the growing human being, as long as it is the concern of the physical body, we should pay close attention to what the healthy desire and joy require. Pleasure and delight are the forces which call forth the physical forms of the organs in the right way.

In this matter it is all too easy to do great harm by failing to bring the child into a right relationship physically with its environment, especially as regards his instincts for food. The child may be overfed with things that make him lose completely his healthy instinct for food. Whereas by giving him the right food the instinct can be so preserved that he always wants what is good for him according to the circumstances, even to a glass of water, and turns from what would be harmful to him. Spiritual science will be able to give detailed indications as regards all sorts of food, if it is called upon to build up an art of education. It is a realistic thing concerning the whole of life and not merely a theory, for which no doubt it could sometimes be mistaken, because of the aberrations of some of our members.

THE TEMPERAMENTS

From: *Discussions with Teachers.*
Extract from:
The Second Discussion   Stuttgart, 22nd August 1919

If children are overfed — and this applies especially to phlegmatic children — you will not be able to teach them anything. Sanguine children should not be given too much meat and phlegmatic children not too many eggs. Melancholic children, on the other hand, can have a good mixed diet but not too many roots nor too much cabbage. For melancholic children diet is very individual and that you will have to watch. With regard to sanguine and phlegmatic children it is possible to generalise.

DIET AND LEARNING TO READ AND WRITE

From: *Discussions with Teachers.*
Extract from:
The Eighth Discussion   Stuttgart, 29th August 1919

If you notice right from the beginning that a child has little talent for reading and writing you would do well to ask the parents to keep the child off eggs, puddings and pastry as far as possible.... For a time they might even cut down the meat and give him plenty of vegetable food and nourishing salads. You will then notice that by dieting the child in this way he will become considerably more able.... You must keep him very busy when his diet is first changed.

But if this mere change of diet is not effective then, after consultation with the parents, try for a short time, say for a week, to keep the child without food for the whole of the morning or at any rate for the first part when he should be learning to read and write. Let him learn on an empty stomach, or at least on the minimum of food. (You should not go on too long with this method; you must alternate it with normal feeding.) But you must make good use of this time ... he will show greater ability and be more receptive.... If you repeat a cure of this sort several times in the course of a year you will see a great change.... This applies to the first years of school life....

Speaking generally you should be aware that the foolish way many parents feed their young children contributes a great deal to the dimunition of their faculties especially with phlegmatic and sanguine children. The perpetual overfeeding of children, stuffing them with eggs and puddings and starchy foods is one of the things which make children unwilling to learn and incapable of doing so in the early years of their school life.

(Following a query about cocoa) Why should children drink cocoa at all? It is not in the least necessary except to regulate digestion. Things of this sort are sometimes needed for this purpose and cocoa is better than other remedies for children whose digestion works too quickly. It should not otherwise be included in children's diet. Nowadays children are given many things which are unsuitable for them.

(Rudolf Steiner gave an example of a pale, thin boy who was given a glass of red wine with his meals and who later, by the time he was in his thirties, had become a very restless and nervous man. He had been a gifted child but never wanted to learn properly. As a result of the wine, he had been ruined by the time he was seven years old.)

34

TEACHING CHILDREN ABOUT NUTRITION

From: *Practical Advice to Teachers.*
Extract from: Lecture 14   Stuttgart, 5th September 1919

You will find that children, when they have not been spoilt in their very first years, have still, relatively speaking, very sound instincts. They have not then acquired the craving to stuff themselves with sweets and so on. They still have certain sound instincts as regards their food as of course has the animal because it is still very much dominated by its body. The animal, just because it is limited to its body, avoids what is harmful to it. The animal world is not likely to be overrun by any evil like the spread of alcoholic consumption in the human world. The spread of evils such as alcohol is due to the fact that man is so much a spiritual being that he can become independent of his bodily nature. For physical nature, in its reasonableness, is never tempted to become alcoholic. Comparatively sound food instincts are active in the first years at school. These cease with the last years of school life in the interests of human development. When puberty comes upon the individual he loses his food instincts; he must find in his reason a substitute for his earlier instincts. That is why you can still catch the last manifestation of the food and health instincts of the growing being in the last years of lower school.

Later, you can no longer find an inner feeling for the right care of food and health. That is why particularly the last years of the lower school should include instruction in nutrition and the care of personal health. Object lessons can reinforce the fantasy or imagination quite considerably. Put before the child three different substances... any substance which is composed primarily of starch or sugar, a substance composed primarily of fat, and a substance composed primarily of protein. The child knows these, but remind him that the human body owes its activity primarily to these three constituents. From this explain to him in his last years in the lower school the secrets of nutrition. Then give him an accurate description of the breathing and enlarge on every aspect of nutrition and breathing connected with the care of personal health. You will gain an enormous amount in your education and teaching if you undertake this instruction precisely in these years. At this stage you are just in time to catch the last instinctive manifestations of the health and food instincts. That is why you can teach the child about nutrition and health at this age without making him egoistic for the rest of his life. It is still natural to him to satisfy instinctively the conditions of health and nutrition. They still strike a chord in his natural life and so do not make him egoistic. If children are not taught about these things in these years they will have to inform themselves later from books or other people. What is learnt later, after puberty, regarding nutrition and health makes people egoistic. It cannot but produce egoism. If you read about nutrition in physiology, if you read rules about the care of health, the very nature of this information makes you more egoistic than you were before. This egoism which continually proceeds from a rationalised knowledge of how to take personal care of oneself, has to be combatted by morality.... But the human being is less exposed to the dangers of egoism in later life if he is instructed in nutrition and health in the last years of the lower school. It is then natural to him.

TASTE. THE TEMPERAMENTS.
LOSS OF INTEREST IN FOOD.

From: *Lectures to Teachers*
Extract from: The 15th Lecture of the full German Edition.
Dornach, 6th January 1922

In the physical realm of the education of the child, three things are very important: diet, temperature and exercise. Everything concerning the physical body belongs to one of these three categories. . . .

It is essential that the teacher, in spite of the influence of science today, preserves a natural instinct for what is healthy and unhealthy. . . .

We have seen that before the change of teeth a child lives predominantly in its physical organism. This is particularly so with the baby, especially as regards food. Its diet is very monotonous when it first comes into the world. To a grown person it would be intolerable, both mentally and physically, to live like this always on the same food. The grown-up wants change. The baby gets no change, but few people can imagine the joy a baby gets out of this food. The whole body becomes saturated with intense sweetness from the mother's milk.

The grown-up person only tastes with his palate and neighbouring organs. He has the bad luck that all the sensations of taste are concentrated in the region of the unfortunate head. This distinguishes him from the child which, as a baby, is through and through an organ of taste. When the baby is weaned this comes to an end. . . . We must develop an understanding for what is palatable to the child and what is not. This is a good guide as to what is health-

188

giving and what is bad for it. For this one needs a good understanding of nutrition in general.

Today one is mainly concerned with the quantity of food, but quantity is not what matters. The essential thing is that man takes in a certain sum of forces in his food. Every food contains certain forces which connect it to the outer world. Within the human organism everything is different. The organism has to completely transform the foodstuffs. Man has to transform the processes within the food into the processes which he needs in his own organism. There is constantly this struggle. The reaction within us against foodstuffs is what stimulates us and keeps us alive. This is why it is no good asking: Must we eat this or that and how much of it? But rather: How does our organism react to even a small amount of any substance? The organism needs these forces to develop resistance to the outer processes of nature.

The processes which go on between the mouth and stomach are comparable, though somewhat modified, to the processes to be found in the outer world. But those which come after the stomach are very different and those in the head system are the exact opposite of external nature processes. Food has the task of stimulating the entire organism of man.

There are foods which are called nourishing and others which are considered non-nourishing. People are brought up on both kinds of food. One need only think how many people have to grow up on a diet of mainly bread and potatoes. These are certainly non-nourishing foods. With a precarious state of health one must be careful not to over-load the digestive system with non-nourishing food. Bread and potatoes are very demanding on the digestive system so that little is left over for the other functions. The growth of the child will not be promoted by such a diet. One must give food which does not overload the digestive system. It will then not have much work to do. If one takes this to extremes then there will be too much activity in the brain. Processes then develop which bear little resemblance to processes in outer nature, and this works back on the rest of the organisation and the digestive system becomes slack and inactive. . . .

Imagine a child eats a potato. It tastes the potato in its head i.e. with its organs of taste and this taste has its effect. Although it does not penetrate the whole organism, yet it affects the whole organism. The potato has not much taste and therefore it leaves the organism to a certain extent indifferent. It does not take much notice of what happens to the potato in the mouth. Then the potato goes on its way to the stomach. The stomach is not particularly interested because it has not been warned by the taste. The stimulating taste always induces the stomach to receive its food with greater or lesser sympathy. With the potato the stomach is not particularly anxious to exert itself to direct it into the organism. But this has to be done. The potato cannot remain in the stomach. If the stomach is strong enough it takes up the potato with aversion, lets it roll down into it, does not react very much and is not much stimulated. The whole thing goes on into the rest of the digestive system and is worked upon with aversion. Extraordinarily little reaches the head. These few comments, which need to be elaborated further, can show you how complicated all these things are which take place in the human organism.

* * * * *

Supposing, in school, one has a child with a tendency towards a melancholic temperament. If this appears in an exaggerated form, one can always be sure that there is a physical abnormality in the child's organisation. Abnormalities of the life of the soul are always based on a physical abnormality in one way or another, for the physical is an expression of the soul/spirit. Suppose one has such a child, one should ask the parents to put one and a half or twice as much sugar in its food as for a normal child. One should advise the parents to be generous with sugar even if one has to give it in the form of sweets.*

Now what do I want to convey? It may become clearer if I describe another case. Let us suppose we have a pathologically sanguine child. It must be an abnormal pathological case if what I am going to say is applicable. So we have an excessively sanguine child. Again there will be an abnormality in the physical organisation, and I will ask the parents to cut down on sugar in the child's food and altogether be very sparing with sugar.

Why should I do this? One only sees to what extent one has to do such a thing if one understands the following. You see the mother's milk, in fact all milk and milk products, influence the whole body uniformly. All the organs get what they need in a harmonious balance through milk and milk products, while all other foods have the pecularity that they each have a predominant influence on one system of organs. Please note that I do not say an exclusive influence, but a predominant one. The question of how a child's sense of taste is related to all kinds of food and how this sense of taste can be taken into consideration depends on how a particular system of organs is constituted.

With milk the whole of man is provided for, but with any other food it is only one system of organs. With sugar, in this particular context, it is the liver which is particularly concerned. Now what am I trying to do if I give a lot of sugar to the abnormally melancholic child? I bring it about that the liver's activity is somewhat reduced, because the sugar in this case takes over the activity of the liver, in a certain sense, so that the liver's own activity is replaced by something which comes from without. In this way I can by

(* Provided these are made of real sugar and not synthetic sweetening. *Translator's note.*)

191

nutrition counteract to a certain extent the melancholic tendency of the child (which can also appear as a tendency to anaemia) which in certain circumstances is due to the liver. What do I do if I restrict sugar in the case of an excessively sanguine child? I try to restrict the activity of the sugar and thus oblige the liver to become more active. I cause the child to arouse its ego and so overcome what is the physical counterpart of the sanguine temperament.

* * * * *

The manifestation of interest is chiefly connected with the metabolic system. If a child loses interest in its mental activities as well as in outer activities, play, etc. or what can be worse — loses interest in the taste of its food — (a child should be really interested in how things taste and in the different tastes of individual foods) if a child loses its appetite (loss of appetite is loss of interest in the physical realm) then one knows that the diet is wrong and overtaxes the digestive system. One must find out how this child's organisation has been overfed with un-nourishing foods. As a barometer indicates the weather, so loss of appetite indicates wrong diet. I must insist that the interest or lack of interest in food should be taken very seriously and should be taken as a guide to the food a child needs.

If however a child is able to eat but gets into a dreamy state after it has eaten and has an abnormal longing to rest, like a snake does after a meal, it is tired out by its digestion. In this case one knows that the child has been given food which does not demand enough of the digestive system and which is mainly worked upon by the head and therefore tires the child.

If a child suffers from loss of interest it should be given so-called nourishing foods. One should not be fanatical. Vegetarian fanatics will say: 'Ah, you see the child lost interest because you fed it on meat. Now you will have to

get it accustomed to raw fruit. Then it will regain its interest.'
This is of course quite possible. On the other hand the meat
eaters will say when a child gets easily tired: 'You will have
to stimulate it with meat.' There is no need to go to either
extreme. It is quite possible to make up diets which would,
for instance, avoid meat. On the other hand it is not so
important to make someone a complete vegetarian. But
what is important is to know that for lack of interest one
has to give more nourishing foods and for fatigue one has
to work in another direction....

Warmth and nourishment are interrelated, so if a child
seems over-susceptible to changes of temperature it should
be given more warming foods. This will make him inwardly
more resistant to the effects of changing temperatures.

CHILD NUTRITION. SUGAR AND POTATOES

From: *Human Values in Education.*
Extract from: Lecture 7   Arnheim, 23rd July 1924

We must know that every manifestation of melancholy in a child, however unlikely it may seem to the physiologist, is connected with some irregularity in the function of the liver. In such a case I would turn to the parents of the child and say: 'You must put more sugar into this child's food. Its food must be sweeter than you normally make it because sugar helps to normalise the function of the liver.' And by giving the mother this advice: 'Give the child more sugar' I shall get school and home working together, in order to raise this melancholy from the pathological condition and so create the possibility of finding the appropriate treatment.

Or perhaps I have a sanguine child who jumps from impression to impression, who always wants the next thing when he has still got the previous one, who has a keen interest for everything which, however, soon lapses. He is not dark as a rule, but fair. I shall have to find how to deal with him at school.... I then get in touch with the mother. She is sure to tell me that the child has an inordinately sweet tooth, that he gets a lot of sweets — or sneaks them. Or he comes from a home where the food is excessively sweetened, and if this is not the case, then the mother's milk was too sweet and contained too much sugar. So I explain to the mother that for a time she must give the child a diet which contains less sugar. In this way co-operation is brought about between home and school. The reduction of sugar will gradually help to overcome the abnormality which, in the case of this child also, is caused by irregularity in the activity of the liver. The secretion of gall is not quite normal. There is a very slight, barely noticeable irregularity in the secretion of gall. Here too I shall recognise the help given me by the parents.

* * * * *

We can go into more detail and say: A child understands quickly, he grasps everything very easily, but after a few days, what he grasped so quickly and about which I was so pleased, has vanished and is no longer there. Here again I can do a good deal at school to improve matters.... But now once more I get in touch with the parents and from them I may hear various things.... I shall find out what the family eats and I shall most likely discover that this particular child eats too many potatoes. This is a tricky situation because the mother may say: 'Well, you tell me that my child eats too many potatoes, but my neighbour's little girl eats even more and she has not the same fault, so it cannot be the potatoes.' The mother will say this. Nonetheless, it *does* come from eating potatoes because the organisation of children differs, one being able to cope with more potato than another. So it happens that this child has been getting too many potatoes for its particular organisation. The result is that his memory does not function as it should. Now in this case the remedy is not to give fewer potatoes. Cutting down potatoes might help for a time but soon things are no better than before. It is not the actual reduction of the amount of potato that helps, but the gradual weaning, the actual activity of giving up. So one must say to the mother: 'In the first week give the child a very little less potato, in the second week a little less again, and so on, so that the child is actively engaged in gradually coming down to eating a much smaller quantity of potato. It is the weaning that matters in this case, and one can see what a healing effect this will have.'

195

Now so-called idealists very likely reproach anthroposophy with being materialistic. They actually do so. When anthroposophy says for instance that a child who grasps easily but does not remember, should have his potato ration gradually reduced, then people say: You are an absolute materialist. But there exists such an intimate interplay between matter and spirit that one can only work effectively when one can see through matter and master it by means gained by spiritual knowledge. It is hardly necessary to say how greatly these things are sinned against in our present-day social life. But if a teacher is open to a world conception which reveals wide vistas, these things come to him. He must only extend his outlook. For instance it will help a teacher to gain an understanding of children if he learns how little sugar is eaten in Russia and how much in England. And if he proceeds to compare the Russian with the English temperament he will no doubt see what an effect sugar has on temperament. One should learn to know the world so that this knowledge can help us in the tasks of every day....

The potato was introduced into Europe in comparatively recent times. And now I will tell you something about which you can laugh as much as you like. Nevertheless it is the truth. One can study the development of human intellectual faculties from the time when there were no potatoes to the time after their introduction. (Potatoes are also used in distilleries for making spirits.) Potatoes, at a certain time, began to play a particular role in the development of European humanity. If you compare the increasing use of the potato with the curve of the development of intelligence, you will find that in comparison with today, people in the pre-potato era grasped things less quickly and readily, but what they grasped they really knew. Their nature was more conservative, profound and reflective. After the introduction of the potato people became quicker in taking up ideas, but what they took in was not retained, it did not sink in deeply. The history of the development of the intelligence runs parallel

196

with that of potato-eating. So here is another example of how anthroposophy explains things 'materialistically'. But so it is. Much might be contributed to cultural history if one always knew how, in his subconscious, man's spiritual nature is influenced by external material things. This appears in his desires.

* * * * *

The potato makes great demands on the digestion. Very small almost homoeopathic doses find their way into the brain. But these homoeopathic quantities are very potent, they spur on the forces of abstract intelligence. Here I may perhaps disclose something interesting. If we examine the substance of the potato under the microscope we find the well-known forms of carbohydrates. If one observes the astral body of someone who has eaten rather a lot of potatoes we notice that in the brain, 3 centimetres behind the forehead, the potato substance begins to be active also in eccentric circles like those seen under the microscope. The movements of the astral body begin to show a similarity to the potato substance and the person becomes extraordinarily intelligent. He bubbles over with intelligence, but it does not last, it is transient. Provided one concedes that man possesses spirit and soul, must one not admit that it is not altogether foolish and fantastic to speak of the spirit and to speak of it in images taken from the world of sense? Anyone who speaks of the spirit only in abstract images does not present us with anything of the nature of spirit. It is otherwise with someone who can bring down the spirit into sense-perceptible pictures. Such a person can say that in someone bubbling over with intelligence, potato substance arises in the brain, but spiritually. Thus one learns to recognise subtle differences and variations. We discover that tea as regards its effects on logic chops up thoughts, but it does not stimulate the creation of thoughts. The fact that diplomats like tea does

197

not imply that they can produce thoughts. The potato stimulates thoughts to flash up and disappear again. But accompanying this swift upsurging of thoughts, which can also take place in children, there goes a parallel process — an undermining of the digestive system. One can see in children whose digestive system is upset in this way so that they complain of constipation, that all kinds of mischievous and clever thoughts flash into their heads, which they lose again, but they were there.

37

APPETITES AND ANTI-APPETITES

From: *Spiritual Science and Medicine.*
Extract from: Lecture 17   Dornach, 8th April 1920

Questions of diet are important because they have social as well as medical implications. One may spend endless time discussing whether the dietetic rules of Mazdaism or other special schools and creeds have any significance or justification. One can of course discuss this but it has to be realised that with all these recommendations a person becomes an unsocial being. Social problems combine with medical ones. The more we are compelled or advised to have some extra kind of food — or altogether anything special — the more unsocial we become. The significance of the Last Supper is that Christ gave the same to all of his disciples and not something special to each one. Making it possible to be together as human beings when eating or drinking has a great social significance, and anything that might tend to repress this healthy natural tendency should be treated with some caution. If a person is left to himself, not only in things he is conscious of but also with regard to his organic processes, he will develop all kinds of appetites and anti-appetites. Attention to these individual appetites and anti-appetites need not be given the importance usually bestowed on them. I am not speaking only of subjective likes and dislikes but of constitutional aversions. If a man has become able to tolerate something which does not really agree with him — that is to say, if an anti-appetite (in the wider sense, speaking of the whole system) has been overcome — then that person has gained more for his organisation than he would have by the constant avoidance of what is antipathetic. The overcoming of something that does not agree with one means the reconstruction of an organ which has been ruined or, seen from the etheric, becomes a new organ. *The organic formative force* consists of nothing less than the overcoming of antipathies. To gratify appetites beyond a certain limit is not to serve and strengthen our organs but to hypertrophise them and bring about their degeneration. To go too far in yielding to the antipathies of an organism which, because of its damages, wants to avoid what it dislikes, causes injury to the organisation. While on the other hand, if one tries gradually to get a person used to what seems unsuitable to him, one always strengthens the organisation.

* * * * *

METABOLISM

From: *Zur Therapie*.
Extract from:
a Lecture to Doctors   Dornach, 31st December 1923

Let us consider metabolism in general. It is under the influence of the astral body and what we usually call metabolism is an activity of the human organism and it is the activity which matters. Metabolism only consists of taking in and excreting substances. The actual substance of the food does not interest the metabolism, but only the overcoming of the form of the substance taken in and its metamorphosis — not what the organism gets out of it. Excretion starts almost immediately with the process of metabolism. Intake is followed almost at once by excretion. Only very little is taken out and this goes right into the nerve/sense organisation. The substance of the nerve/sense organisation is extraordinarily important, for the nerve substance is the end product of metabolism.

Grotesque as it may seem, the contents of the intestines are in reality nerve substance remaining unfinished in a halfway state. The nerve substance, mainly in the head, is intestinal contents brought to its final state. It is transformed by the human organism, above all, by the ego organisation. The contents of the intestine are arrested and excreted in a halfway state. The nerve substance has reached a final stage, and this used-up stuff has been completely transformed by the organism.

THE ROLE OF PROTEIN IN THE HUMAN BODY

From: *Fundamentals of Therapy,* by Rudolf Steiner and Ita Wegman.
Extract from: Chapter 9   First published in 1925

Protein is the substance which the formative forces of the living body transform in the most manifold ways, and the result of this transformed substance appears in the forms of the organs and the whole organism. To be used in this way protein must have the inherent faculty of relinquishing any form that might be due to the nature of its material constituents. It must be able to do this the moment it is required to serve a form which the organism demands.

From this one can see that in protein the forces and mutual relationships of hydrogen, oxygen, nitrogen and carbon disintegrate. The inorganic combinations of substances cease in the disintegration of protein and the organic formative forces start to work.

The formative forces are a function of the etheric body. Protein is always about to be received into the activity of the etheric body or to drop out of it. Removed from the living organism to which it once belonged, it assumes the tendency to become a compound which subjects itself to the inorganic forces of hydrogen, oxygen, nitrogen and carbon. Protein which remains part of the living organism suppresses this tendency and becomes subject to the formative forces of the etheric.

Man eats protein as part of his food. The pepsin of the stomach transforms this protein into peptones which are at first soluble substances. The transformation is then continued by the pancreatic juice.

The protein thus taken in as a constituent of food is, to begin with, a foreign body in the human organism. It contains the after-effects of the etheric processes of the living being whence it was derived. These have to be entirely eliminated, for it now has to be received into the etheric activity of the human organism.

Thus in the course of the process of digestion we have to do with two different kinds of protein substances. At the beginning of the digestive process the protein is foreign to the human organism: at the end it is part of it. Between these two conditions there is an intermediate one where the protein taken in as food has not yet entirely discarded its former etheric influences nor yet entirely assumed the new. At this stage it is almost completely inorganic. It is then only under the influence of the human physical body. The physical body of man, which in its form is moulded by the ego-organisation, possesses inorganic forces. It therefore kills what is alive. Everything that enters the realm of the ego-organisation has to die. Hence in the physical body the ego-organisation incorporates purely inorganic substances. Though in the physical organism of man they do not work in the same way as in the external lifeless world of nature, yet their action is nevertheless inorganic, i.e. it kills what is alive. This killing action upon the living protein takes place in that part of the digestive tract where trypsin — a constituent of the pancreatic juice — is active.

That inorganic forces are concerned in the action of trypsin may be seen also from the fact that it unfolds its activity in the presence and with the help of alkali.

Until it meets the trypsin in the pancreatic fluid, protein continues to live in the same way as it lived in the organism from which it originated. When it meets the trypsin it becomes lifeless. But, however, only for a moment is it lifeless in the human organism. At that moment it is taken up by the physical body directed by the ego-organisation. This latter must have strength to carry over what the protein has become into the realm of the human etheric body. In this way the protein becomes material for building the human organism. The foreign etheric influence which it formerly carried leaves the human being.

* * * * *

40

THE ROLE OF FAT IN THE HUMAN ORGANISM

From: *Fundamentals of Therapy*, by Rudolf Steiner and Ita Wegman.

Extract from: Chapter 10   First published in 1925

Of all substances taken into the organism from outside, fat behaves least of all as a foreign substance. More readily than any other substance it passes from its own nature to that of the human organism. The 80% of fat contained for instance in butter passes unchanged by ptyalin and pepsin and is only transformed by the pancreatic juice into glycerine and fatty acids.

This behaviour of fat is made possible because it carries as little as possible of the nature of a foreign organism (i.e. its etheric forces etc.) into the human organism. The latter can easily absorb it into its own activity.

This is due to the fact that fat plays a special part in the production of inner warmth. This warmth is the element of the physical organism in which the ego-organisation mainly lives. The ego is only concerned with as much of *any* substance as can be transformed into warmth. Fat shows by its behaviour that it merely fills out the body, is carried by the body, and is important for the active organisation only as far as those processes which produce warmth. Fat that comes for instance from an animal organism, takes nothing over into the human except its inherent capacity to produce heat or warmth.

Now this production of warmth is one of the last processes of metabolism. Fat taken as food remains therefore unchanged by the earlier processes of metabolism and is only absorbed further on by the activity of the pancreatic fluid.

The presence of fat in human milk points to a very significant activity of the organism. The body does not consume this fat itself but allows it to become a product of secretion. The ego-organisation enters into *this* fat. This gives the formative force to the mother's milk. The mother thereby transmits her own formative forces of the ego-organisation to the child, and thus adds something more to the formative forces already transmitted by heredity.

It is healthy and normal when, in the development of warmth, the human form-giving forces consume all the fat that is present in the body. On the other hand it is unhealthy if the fat is not used up by the ego-organisation in its warmth processes, but carried over unused into the organism. Such fat will offer innumerable possibilities of creating heat in various places in the organism. This heat is then irritating to the other life-processes of the organism and is not under the control of the ego-organisation. There arise, as it were, parasitic centres of heat, predisposing to inflammatory conditions. The origin of these lies in the fact that the body develops a tendency to make more fat than the ego-organisation requires for its life within the inner warmth.

In the healthy organism the animal (astral) forces will produce or take up as much fat as the ego-organisation is able to transmute into warmth processes and, in addition, as much as is required to keep the mechanism of muscle and bone in order. In this case the right amount of warmth for the body's needs will be produced. If the animal forces supply the ego-organisation with an insufficient quantity of fat, it will be starved of warmth and thus obliged to withdraw the warmth it needs from the activities of the organs. The latter then become in a sense brittle and hardened. Their necessary functions become sluggish. Morbid processes may occur here and there, and in order to understand them it will be necessary to recognise if and how they are due to a general deficiency of fat.

If there is an excess of fat giving rise to parasitic centres

206

of heat, certain organs will be forced into an activity beyond their normal measure. Tendencies will arise to eat too much and so overload the organism. It is however not absolutely necessary that such a person eats undue quantities. It may be, for instance, that the metabolic activity of the organism supplies too much substance to an organ in the head, withdrawing it from organs of the lower body and from the secretory processes. The activity of the deprived organs will then be reduced. The secretions of the glands, for instance, may become deficient. The relative proportions of the body fluids can become unhealthy. For instance, the secretion of bile may become excessive compared to that of the pancreatic fluid. It will be important to recognise how a localised complex of symptoms arising from an unhealthy fat metabolism should be assessed.

PART III

From an early lecture given to
Members of the Theosophical Society

Appendices a) and b).

41

DIFFERENT FORMS OF NOURISHMENT
IN HUMAN EVOLUTION

From: *Foundations of Esotericism.*
Extracts from: Lecture 30   Berlin, 4th November 1905

There was a time when human beings were able to draw nourishment from their immediate environment, just as our lungs draw air today. Man was formerly connected with the whole surrounding nature by 'suction-threads' and nourished in a somewhat similar way as the human embryo is in the mother's womb today.... The process of suckling in mammals is the relic of it. Milk is like the food taken by man in pre-Lemurian times. It is the old food of the gods — the first form of nourishment on earth....

There was a time when humanity was directly connected with the animal nature, immersed in it and nourished by it. We can get an idea of this if we think of how mammals feed their young with their own milk....

In the pre-Lemurian epoch conditions were such that milk was drawn from the surroundings. Then came the epoch when milk was the general food of man, and then an epoch when mother's milk was taken....

When the sun separated from the earth the plants... turned their flowers towards the sun. The part of the plant which grows above the surface of the earth is related to the sun as milk is related to the moon. A kind of plant-food, consisting of the upper parts of plants gradually replaced milk. This was the second kind of human food.

Let us now pass from the Lemurian to the Atlantean epoch....: Among the Atlanteans something appeared that was not there before. They began for the first time to nourish themselves with something that is not drawn from life. They began to feed on what is dead, that which has relinquished life. This was a very important transition in human existence. It was the transition to egohood. Man consumed the dead in its different forms. They became hunters. Others appeared who consumed not only what had been ripened by the sun, but also what ripened below the surface of the earth itself. That is just as lifeless as the dead animal.... Later another food was added, a food which previously did not exist. Man added to his food the purely mineral element such as salt, which he took from the earth. Thus with regard to his nourishment, man went through the three kingdoms. This was the path taken by Atlantean evolution.... All these things represent the turning away from the real life forces. What is dead in the animal has turned away from life; the part of the plant that is within the soil has also turned away from life. All salts are the dead elements of the mineral kingdom. They are what have remained behind from the past....

In the post-Atlantean epoch the milk-drinker continues side by side with the fruit eater. Other forms of food are added as something new. What comes to the fore in the post-Atlantean epoch is that mineral matter is obtained by a *chemical* process. This is indicated in Genesis. Noah became intoxicated by wine. It denotes an ascent in evolution when a chemical process is applied to plants. *Wine* is produced.... Wine plays a particular role in the post-Atlantean epoch.... But the Indian, Persian and Egyptian initiates used no wine. *Water* was used in their sacred rites. It was only gradually that wine began to play a part... for instance in the cult of Dionysus.

It was in the fourth culture-epoch (the Graeco-Latin) that Christianity arose and the mission of this epoch was foreshadowed 700 years earlier in the festivals of Dionysus where wine was introduced into the cult. In a wonderful way the evangelist who knew most about Christianity, St.

John, portrayed this fact. At the beginning of his Gospel he tells of the changing of water into wine.... A teaching was needed which hallowed the descent to the physical plane. Wine severs the human being from all spirituality. This had to be. In the whole course of the evolution of humanity there is descent and ascent. Man had at one time to descend to the lowest point.... If humanity were to ascend again, it must have a symbol which leads again from the dead to the living: bread and wine....

What is to develop in the future is a further ascent from plant food to mineral food. Bread and wine will have to be sacrificed, to be given up. Christ came in the 4th cultural epoch and he pointed to bread and wine, indicating that it was a transition from meat to plant-food, a transition to something higher....

After our present 5th culture-epoch has come to an end, then, in the 6th culture-epoch, the meaning of the Eucharist will be understood. There will then be no eating of meat. Between now and then it will become possible to develop the *third* form of nourishment, purely mineral nourishment. Man will then be able to create his food himself. First of all he consumed what the gods prepared for him; later on he will advance and will himself prepare in the laboratory the food he needs.... In the same measure in which he produces his own food out of his own wisdom — the god within — he advances towards his own deification.... Man will gradually create life for himself out of the mineral world. What the scientist knows today is only a fraction of the great cycle.

Appendix (a)

MILLING AND BAKING

Compiled by Fr. Schyre from indications given by Rudolf
Steiner on various occasions. (From *Mitteilungen des
Landwirtschaftlichen Versuchsringes der Anthroposophischen
Gesellschaft,** No. 14, 2nd Year, March 1928.)

It is obvious that the anthroposophical farmer does not like
to part with his produce without knowing what becomes of
it. The special love and care bestowed on the fruits of his
fields and his dairy products gives him an inner connection
with them which is not easily severed. He feels responsible
that they should not be carelessly handled and that they
should find their way undamaged to those who are in such
need of them. This feeling of care and responsibility for the
fruits of his land will be the healthy basis of processing
associations or companies.

The most important of the many questions concerning
the processing of crops on their way to the consumer is the
milling and baking of grain. To make a start we have
collected everything that Dr. Steiner said on various occasions
concerning milling and baking. Many of our friends have
gone to much trouble to assemble all this material. Naturally
we cannot expect it to be complete but the essentials seem
to be available. The following is an outline.

Milling
We will try to convey the full force of Dr. Steiner's instructions
and observations. In the process of milling the etheric forces
in the grain must in no way be damaged. Milling is not a

* The News Sheet of the original German Experimental Circle.

purely mechanical process but a biological one comparable with baking and cooking. If one grinds purely mechanically the resulting flour has little nutritive value. Milling should be the joint work of elemental beings and such people who can be befriended by good elemental spirits. The mill is a body built by man of water, stone and wood for well-intentioned elemental spirits who will make grain into flour without reducing its life forces. This is why the interior of a mill bears the character of a temple. In contrast to this in modern mills with turbines, electric motors, and metal construction as well as in roller mills, a quarter or half of the etheric life forces, i.e. the food value of the grain, is lost by the violent mechanical milling.

The important thing is that the grain should not be crushed or violently broken and ground but converted into flour by gentle rubbing between itself and the lightly resting millstones; it should only be rolled around and not crushed.

The Mental Attitude of the Miller

Herr Julius Ritter von Rainer had a mill near Klagenfurt which for several years was run according to Dr. Steiner's ideas. Herr Hamburger from Vienna worked there for one and a half years and writes about it in two very interesting letters.

'The miller must be awake and experience joy and sorrow in inner equilibrium — a mood of meditation approaching a religious attitude. It is an arduous task for the soul and can teach devotion and devoutness. The intellect is used as an instrument. (Piety, courage, reverence.) Someone who enters the mill can feel it. If he enters it with the wrong attitude of mind he can even bring it to a standstill. The true miller is scrupulously clean and always keeps a broom or brush at hand.

'When one has to do with flour and bread-making which is, after all, closely connected with farming upon which earth and man are dependent, it is essential that one takes

212

seriously the striving and devotion to truth and knowledge and inner quietude. It is important for all the workers, but especially for the master. One gains the strength for this by a deep study of *Knowledge of the Higher Worlds*, *Theosophy*, *Occult Science*, *Philosophy of Freedom*, *Towards Social Renewal*, *World Economy*, *The Four Mystery Plays* and everything else that Dr. Steiner has given us. These should be studied on one's own and together with the other workers.'

The master of a concern can only be a person who experiences inwardly what goes on within his whole field of work and tries to keep this in accord with his own self and the whole world. Then he will always be on the spot when something goes wrong.

When setting up a mill and bakery which are concerned with something that is alive, technology and commercial considerations must consciously only be used as tools in the right place. They must absolutely lose the sovereignty they enjoy today. One could be a little uneasy and wonder if the mill would come to a standstill if one entered it just as one is. One feels particularly strongly the demands which arise from every one of these words of Dr. Steiner's: 'advance continually in your moral development....' Only because of the urgency of what has to be achieved may one presume, already today, to take on the tasks which arise from the work of Dr. Rudolf Steiner.

If one tries to imagine the kind of mill which would fulfil Dr. Steiner's ideas, the image of an old mill dreaming by the side of a burbling stream rises up in the mind. But this picture must be stripped of the romantic beauty of an old mill falling into decay. It is not a question of realising a romantic ideal, but what we want is to mill grain without losing one third or a half of its nutritive value.

Quality of the Flour
It will be necessary to show indubitably what an enormous

213

difference there is between flour milled according to Dr. Steiner's advice and flour produced by the squashing action of roller mills. Observations made by Herr Hamburger and by Konradin Hausser show that flour produced in the proper way has almost twice as much life-giving forces in its substance as flour milled in roller mills. Herr Hamburger writes:

'To make 'Schmarren' (a stiff batter fried and cut in pieces) for one working man we only needed 100 grams of flour, whereas with today's flour one normally reckons 200 grams. With our own flour there was a great saving of fat. I had some flour which was a year old, and to make the basis of a white sauce it needed only half the amount of fat compared with ordinary flour. We did not need to use any eggs when baking a 'Gugelhupf' (a cake in a ring mould) made of wheat flour with salt, sugar and milk, it had a brownish reddish gold colour. We never used eggs, even in pancakes.'

Herr Konradin Hausser writes: 'Our regular experience at the 'Guldesmühle' was that we only ate two thirds of the quantity of bread when made of our own flour, compared with what we needed when we had bread from Stuttgart or somewhere else.' If to the different milling we add the advantage of grain grown without artificial fertilisers, the effect is very noticeable and easy to prove.

The Internal Construction of the Mill
The correct milling process depends above all upon the spindle and socket. 'The mill must turn very easily. The spindle must be so adjusted that the runner stone turns on the bed-stone, rumbling contentedly. It should be possible to grind on two mills in case one has to be cleaned or needs repair. The mill must be centred in the heart of the miller where the equilibrium of the whole concern is created ever anew. Every mill must run easily. The transmission from the cog wheel to the spindle should be in the proportion of 7 to 12 or 12 to 7. The spindle shaft (Spindelstock) has the

214

sanctity of a temple. The spindle must be so adjusted that the runner stone turns on the bed-stone, rumbling contentedly. The choice of stone is tremendously important. There should be two mills, one for rye, the other for wheat, barley, maize and buckwheat. It is difficult to find the right stones. The stone for rye has to be hard and coarse grained (conglomerate is possible). The stone for wheat must be even harder but fine grained. Rhythm compensates for a certain amount of power. The mill must be based on this principle.

'There must be a harmonious proportion between the flow of water, the mill wheel and the size of the stones. This can only be determined on the individual site. A mill is incredibly sensitive. When it is working everything can get out of order if the wrong person comes in. Everything depends on the dedication of the miller and his helpers. The elemental spirits are present and participate.

'I forgot to mention the importance of the triple rhythm. The fine adjustment of the mill must be left to the feeling of the miller. The runner stone should only just touch the grain. The milling itself is done by the grains rubbing and jostling each other. This is a bit of a mystery which to me is not quite understandable. The mill must be kept very clean — use broom and brush!

'A mill consists of a waterwheel, an axle, a transmission system, spindle, two stones, chute and sieves. The wheel in Mageregg rotated 20 times per minute and the stone 20 x 7 (i.e. 140 times per minute). The bed-stone has to be harder than the runner stone.'

There should be a little play between the parts of the mill. It should not be too rigid. 'The axle which carried the waterwheel and the pit wheel (56 teeth) rested on two bearings. A large cog engaged the spindle cog which had the shape of a round temple with 7 pillars.* The upper end of

* This seems obscure to the translators since they could not find such a shape in an English watermill.

the spindle was shaped like a truncated pyramid on which the runner stone rested. The stones in Mageregg were 75cm. in diameter. As regards the other parts, it is best to study them in a working mill.

'I would like to repeat that the stones must run very easily with a contented rumble in which one can detect three beats: rum, rum, rum.' (contributed by Herr Hausser.)

About the milling process, Herr Hamburger says:

Milling Process

'The passage of one hopper of grain through the stones is called a run. Each hopper-full has to go through the stones four times. The first run cleans the grain. The stones are set so that the grain only loses its tip which, together with dust, etc. falls into the sieve and is discarded. The cleaned grain comes out ready to be milled. The next run must be so adjusted that the grain is broken; not much flour is produced. The next two runs produce all the flour. The test of good milling is that the bran falls off in large flakes, completely free from flour. When I milled for the first time I only got 56% of flour! Later on it was 65% and with practice 75% and even 82%. Loss in dust was 2%. It is not recommended to make semolina because for every 5kg of semolina 75kg of second grade flour is produced.

'The setting of the stones is not easy until one acquires experience. One must learn to run the flour through one's fingers and feel whether the flour is coarse or soft and "smeary". Obviously the dressing of the stones is very important. Successful milling depends on the first run. If this goes wrong, not much can be done. With ordinary intellectual thinking the transformation from grain into flour cannot be grasped.

'After what one has said regarding the life forces in flour it should also be mentioned that flour should not come into contact with metal. One should therefore be critical of mills which include metal parts. Some friends in Stuttgart maintain that Dr. Steiner recommended the use of vertical stones instead of horizontal ones. The flour for Burkhardt bread, for instance, was milled in a Steinmetz mill with vertical discs.'

Steinmetz Mill

The Steinmetz mill works as follows: The grain is slightly damped before milling which enables the skin to peel off. The moisture does not penetrate into the grain so that after peeling off it can be easily ground. This is done between vertical discs. The Steinmetz mill is extraordinarily efficient. A small mill in a room 5 x 6.5 x 3.5 metres, mills 300-400kg of grain per hour. If one compares the Steinmetz mill with the requirements of a good mill as we have described them, one may have doubts about the following: though the discs are made of stone (compound stone) yet the milling process is just as violent as in a roller mill. The source of power is sometimes a waterwheel but usually an electric motor. The Steinmetz mill has the character of a modern machine. Grain and flour come in contact with metal. Whether the peeling of the grain can be compared with the polishing of rice — which is known to be questionable — cannot at present be decided. There seems to be something in the construction of Steinmetz mills which could perhaps be applied to horizontal mills. Where water mills as recommended by Dr. Steiner are not available, Steinmetz mills would be perhaps the best alternative. The Steinmetz mill will have to be tested and compared with horizontal stone mills and roller mills. It must be said that it would be against the intention of Dr. Steiner to set up a mill which is out of date and doomed to be uneconomic. At the Guldesmühle Dr. Steiner was definitely in favour of putting in a turbine.*

On the storage of grain and the even more difficult storage

* A turbine is not necessarily used to produce electric power. The water is merely forced to turn spiralling curved vanes instead of flowing over a large wheel. (Translators' note.)

of flour we have no instructions from Dr. Steiner. We would like to point out the importance of this question because modern storage methods employ some very dubious techniques, such as the use of prussic acid gas to kill meal-worms, mice and other vermin. Here too we must keep our eyes open.

The Baking of Bread

There is a paper in *Naturwissenschaftliche Wochenschrift* 1922, dealing with the historical development of bread making on the basis of which 'guide-lines of civilisation' (according to Müller-Lyers) are laid down. These guide-lines lead to the conclusion that in the future only pure white plain wheat bread will be eaten. But this is written in ignorance of the modern theory of vitamins which, as the result of innumerable experiments, has shown that a diet of pure white bread is unthinkable and leads to severe disorders. This paper on 'guide-lines', however, leads in the wrong direction, as do so many other things which are contributing to the decline of western civilisation. The basic teachings of spiritual science about etheric forces transcend the vitamin theory. This fact can well be understood by the anthroposophist, but one day it will have to be elaborated in a way that will make it accessible to the general public. According to Dr. Steiner the aim of baking is a bread which, on its own, is a complete food for man. In a private conversation in the park at Koberwitz, Dr. Steiner said that the 'Rainer' bread has already fulfilled this requirement. In the production of this complete Rainer bread, the milling of the grain by a water mill was a prerequisite.

Dr. Steiner is also reputed to have said that rye bread and not wheat is the real suitable basis of nutrition in Central Europe. The wheat plant is younger than rye and will die out sooner. Several of our friends confirm Dr. Steiner's insistence that rye bread is particularly important for Central Europeans.

Two different varieties of bread were produced under the personal direction of Dr. Steiner:

1) a simple country loaf like the Rainer bread.
2) a more complicated bread something like the Burkhardt bread.

While it seems difficult to spread the complicated Burkhardt bread beyond anthroposophical circles, it is quite possible to bake a good country bread, approved by Dr. Steiner, for the general public, because there is a longing, even in the towns, for such bread. The making of the bread as done on Ritter von Rainer's place is best described by Herr Hamburger.

'Twenty-four kilos of rye flour, approx. 1.5 kg of leaven (Sauerteig), 12 litres of water, 600 grams of salt made 20 loaves of bread of 1½ kg each, plus 1½ kg of leaven (for next baking). 1.82 kg of dough made a loaf of 1.5 kg. At 6 pm the leaven was dissolved in warm or cold water according to the season, and 5 kg of flour were mixed in by hand. At 1 pm next day, half of the remaining flour was mixed in with the addition of some water. At 4 pm the remaining flour and water was added and the dough was kneaded. The kneading was quite a dramatic affair — exposition, entanglement, climax, loosening of the knots, peripetia (sudden change of fortune). When the dough is smooth and no longer sticks, the battle is over (loosening of the knots). One must be able to take the whole lot out of the trough in one lump. Then it is left to rise in the trough. At about 6 pm the oven is fired. One needs one log 90 cm x 8 to 10 cm per loaf. The wood should have been felled on a waxing moon the previous winter. The wood is piled in the oven and lit. The dough is weighed out and each loaf laid into its straw basket (Simperl) and put on top of the warm oven to rise. When the wood is burnt up the ashes should be white. Then the oven is swept out and could even be quickly wiped with a damp cloth. Now the loaves are turned out of their baskets upside down onto a wooden shovel and put into the oven. The oven is shut tightly. After quarter of an hour the steam is let out by 2 holes high up on either side of the door. After 10 minutes the holes are shut again. At 8 pm or 8.30 pm the bread is ready and is taken out. Baking is a great trial, but one which, however, gives much joy. Everything must fit together to achieve the desired result. For this type of bread one should use only rye or wheat but not both, and one should use leaven, not yeast. Dr. Steiner said one could flavour bread with any of the following: walnuts, aniseed, almonds, fennel seed, hazelnuts or carraway. Our oven only takes 32 loaves. All tools are made of wood.'

From this report one sees again very clearly how in the whole process, in every detail, account is taken of etheric phenomena — the choice of wood, the time it is felled, the time chosen for the rising of the bread — all these things Dr. Steiner passed on to us from his knowledge of the etheric realm.

Countess Polzer-Hoditz confirmed Herr Hamburger's report and added a few points. 'The bread oven should not be made of sheet metal but of brick. Rye bread needs pine logs, wheat bread hardwood — beech. The heat produced has quite different qualities. It is important that the fermentation of the leaven extends over midnight. The leaven should be kept from one baking to the next. It must be warmed up and mixed with water. The flour must also be warmed by standing in a warm room the previous day, likewise the water.' Countess Polzer-Hoditz attached great importance to the keeping quality of the bread. Herr Hamburger writes: 'In a book of the 17th century we read that bread baked at Christmas keeps till Whitsuntide. I tried it out and can confirm it.' Unfortunately, this keeping quality could not always be relied upon. Many friends found that the Burghardt bread often became mouldy and Countess Polzer-Hoditz said about the Rainer bread: 'The flour was marvellous but the bread had one fault, it often went mouldy and I believe this happened when it was sent out too early. Long lasting bread should lie in a straw basket until it is completely cold and should not be stood on its side in racks. Otherwise one gets cracks inside and this is where the mould starts. The baskets are bound with willow and smell like honey if the bread is properly baked.'

Ehrenfried Pfeiffer reports: 'Basically Dr. Steiner's recommendations were always to use leaven, that the fermentation should take place overnight, and baking in the morning. The overnight fermentation has probably to do with the working of the moon forces and the baking takes place when the sun rises. Dr. Steiner indicated the different woods that should be used for different breads: white bread (wheat), beech; brown bread (rye), pine. He obviously thought of the simple farm bread-oven where the wood is burnt inside the oven, the ashes removed, and the bread put in. I consider the use of electric ovens as harmful as electric cookers about which Dr. Steiner has commented.'

Here a definite stand is made against electric baking ovens. Scientific experiments have verified the influence of electricity on etheric formative forces. Wilhelm Pelikan in Schwäbisch Gmünd has concerned himself with such experiments. It is different with steam ovens.

Additional points come from Dr. Rudolf Maier in Einsingen near Ulm. According to his report, bread which is eaten to supplement a meal may be considered in a different way from bread which is a staple food. He says: 'During a conversation with Dr. Steiner at the Guldesmühle certain observations were made. There was a new baking oven which was heated with wood or peat in the oven itself. Following discussions with my doctor, we came to the conclusion that it was essential to bake bread in a space previously filled with the heat of flames. Dr. Steiner, however, said: "For the stomach of a townsman the use of a steam oven would be better. If bread is eaten with a meal, for instance soup, white bread is often better than brown bread. Personally I prefer it."

'Dr. Steiner also concerned himself with the problem of kneading the dough and when asked if the use of machines could be considered, he replied that there was no objection but the machine should be so constructed that it imitates the movements of kneading by hand. The rhythm is particularly important, the number of rotations per minute should not be arbitrary, but a certain natural rhythm should be observed.'

It is fortunate that Dr. Maier remembered so accurately what Dr. Steiner said about kneading (mixing) machines. This removes one undesirable uncertainty about equipping a bakery according to anthroposophical ideas. In a personal conversation with Herr Schofer — who, in Stuttgart, bakes a bread following as closely as possible anthroposophical ideas — it appeared that the work of hand-kneading is too heavy for most people today. It is hardly possible to find people who are able and willing to do it. It would hardly be possible to keep workers in a bakery for any length of time if it were necessary for them to knead large quantities of dough continually. We can also be grateful to Dr. Rudolf Maier for making suggestions as to how to construct such a kneading machine which will be helpful in the future.

While the Rainer bread is a bread made in the traditional farmhouse manner, the ideas behind the Burkhardt bread are an attempt to lead into the future. The Burkhardt bread has the following characteristics:

1) It uses the four principle grains in proportions given by Dr. Steiner.
2) Besides the conventional additions such as fennel, caraway and aniseed, it also contains roasted walnuts and hazelnuts.
3) It is not made with yeast or leaven, but with a rising agent made of honey and salt.

We should like to call attention especially to the use of honey which is very understandable in view of the significance that Dr. Steiner attached to honey for adults (see: *Nine Lectures on Bees* and *Man as Symphony of the Creative Word*.)

Up to now it has not been possible to put into practice all the wealth of suggestions given by Dr. Steiner for the production of Demeter flour and Demeter bread. By far the greater part of the value of the product comes from the way the grain is grown. Considering present-day conditions, we have done all that was possible regarding the milling and baking. If all concerned contribute according to what they are able to do, there is hope that the ideas of Dr. Steiner will be realised increasingly in Demeter products.

Appendix (b)

BREAD-MAKING WITH HONEY
by
Paul Burkhardt

In Northern Germany, bread, especially the solid dark breads, are made with leaven. This way of making bread has been taken over from former civilisations who knew no other way of making bread rise. For the last 150 years white rolls, etc. and in Southern Germany even bread, was usually baked with yeast from distilleries. This is a by-product of the distilling of spirits and some of the larger bakeries made it themselves. Half a loaf of barley bread and half a loaf of rye bread were mashed up in water and left to ferment for a few days. As a result of the alcoholic fermentation, a frothy, fluffy mass consisting of half-disintegrated grain (starch particles) comes to the surface. This was skimmed, allowed to drain and if necessary, mixed with some potato flour to make it firmer and easier to handle. In a similar way, but with more sophisticated techniques, yeast is made today in the large distilleries. During the last decades special institutions were founded for the study of yeasts and they supplied special strains of yeast to the distilleries. Both yeast and leaven produce alcoholic fermentation, the only difference being that leaven has an acid reaction; their proliferation is rather similar. Leaven cells multiply by cell division like distiller's yeast and brewer's yeast. The latter is hardly used for baking but is dried and used as protein and vitamin supplements in animal feeding stuffs. Before yeast and leaven were in use, 'spontaneous fermentation' was known and used about 1,500 years ago in Sweden, Russia, Poland and the Balkans to make 'flat bread'. If one mixes crushed grain with water and leaves this mush in a temperature of between 30°C and 50°C, fermentation agents develop within 8 hours which are capable of more than doubling the volume of the dough. These so-called wild yeasts have been found to belong to the group of bacteria called *coli communi*. They produce carbonic acid but no alcohol.

During the Middle Ages and in Persia, as the modern Mazdaists maintain, it was the custom to make bread with the addition of honey, salt and oil. Even today so-called Masdean bread is produced and sold commercially and goes under the name of 'unfermented bread'. To call it 'unfermented' is of course nonsense. Bread is only 'unfermented' if chemical agents such as cream of tartar, bicarbonate of soda, amonium chloride or hydrogen peroxide are used. Wherever anything baked has holes in it not produced by a chemical rising agent, then fermentation must have taken place, be it spontaneous or due to yeast or leaven.

Some years ago I had the privilege of speaking with Dr. Steiner about bread baking, rising agents, and the procuring of suitable flour. At that time he laid less stress on the fermenting agent but much more on the fact that the whole grain should be used including the germ, the seed coat below the bran and the protein-containing cells (aleuron). From this conversation granted me by our revered and beloved Dr. Steiner arose the Burkhardt bread, and if our anthroposophical friends are interested, I am very willing to discuss the question of bread baking further. For years I have experimented and tried to bake a good loaf using honey and salt. It is known that salt, like calcium, makes the dough lighter and gives the finished loaf a larger volume. The Mazdaists bake so-called 'salt bread'. Their white bread with an excessive amount of salt produces quite a good rising. However, I believe this excessive amount of salt is very harmful. The addition of honey, perhaps together with some oil has a very favourable effect, hastening the spontaneous fermentation and producing a more even rising. It does not form a very hard crust. To 10 kg of wheat flour I add 250 g of honey, ¼ litre of good vegetable oil, 7 litres of water at about 40°C and 150 g of salt. The honey and salt are dissolved in the water and then mixed with the oil and the flour. The dough must be well kneaded for at least one hour. After putting it in the baking tins it must stand for several hours in a warm, draught-free place and is then baked in a medium oven. Baking time at 200°C is 2½ to 3 hours. It is desirable to cover the baking tins in the oven to avoid cracks in the crust, because the spontaneous ferments stand quite a lot of heat and go on working for a while during baking. In bread made with yeast or leaven, fermentation stops at a heat of 50°C which is soon reached. Spontaneous fermentation is only suitable for wholemeal flour and not for white flour.

* * * * *

Translators' note: There is now available a rising agent made by Frau Pokorny in Darmstadt based on honey and salt.

INDEX

The numbers in this index are extract numbers

GERMAN SOURCES OF TEXT
(G.A. is an abbreviation for Gesamtausgabe)

Part I From: Vorträge für die Arbeiter am Goetheanum

Extract	Date	
1	5.8.22	Die Erkenntnis des Menschenwesens nach Leib Seele und Geist. G.A. 347
2	9.8.22	Ibid.
3	13.9.22	Ibid.
4	16.9.22	Ibid.
5	8.1.23	Über Gesundheit und Krankheit. Grundlagen einer geisteswissenschaftlichen Sinneslehre. G.A. 348
6	13.1.23	Ibid.
7	3.2.23	Ibid.
8	5.5.23	Vom Leben der Menschen und der Erde. Über das Wesen des Christentums. G.A. 349
9	18.7.23	Rhythmen im Kosmos und im Menschenwesen. Wie kommt man zum Schauen der geistigen Welt? G.A. 350
10	22.9.23	Ibid.
11	26.11.23	Mensch und Welt. Das Wirken des Geistes in der Natur. Über das Wesen der Bienen. G.A. 351
12	5.12.23	Ibid.
13	10.12.23	Ibid.
14	23.1.24	Natur und Mensch in geisteswissenschaftlicher Betrachtung. G.A. 352
15	16.2.24	Ibid.
16	20.2.24	Ibid.
17	31.7.24	Die Schöpfung der Welt und des Menschen. Erdenleben und Sternenwirkung. G.A. 354
18	2.8.24	Ibid.
19	20.9.24	Ibid.
20	24.9.24	Ibid.

Part II (a) From general lectures

21	22.10.06	Ursprungsimpulse der Geisteswissenschaft. G.A. 96
22	17.12.08	Wo und wie findet man den Geist? G.A. 57
23	8.1.09	(Title not yet decided) (G.A. 68)
24	1.1.12	Die Welt der Sinne und die Welt des Geistes. G.A. 134
25	20.3.13	Welche Bedeutung hat die okkulte Entwicklung des Menschen für seinen Hüllen — physischen Leib, Ätherleib, Astralleib und sein Selbst? G.A. 145
26	21.3.13	Ibid.
27	22.3.23	Die Impulsierung des Weltgeschichtlichen Geschehens durch geistige Mächte. G.A. 222
28	10.11.23	Der Mensch als Zusammenklang des schaffenden, bildenden und gestaltenden Weltenwortes. G.A. 230